This edition published by Parragon Books Ltd in 2014

Parragon Books Ltd
Chartist House
15–17 Trim Street
Bath BA1 1HA, UK
www.parragon.com

ISBN 978-1-4723-6705-1

Printed in China

MONSTER HIGH
Collection

PaRragon

Bath • New York • Cologne • Melbourne • Delhi
Hong Kong • Shenzhen • Singapore • Amsterdam

Frankie Stein™

Draculaura™

Age:
How many days has it been now?
Fave subject:
Hiss-tory
Worst subject:
Swimming – electricity
and water don't mix.
GFFs:
Draculaura and Clawdeen Wolf
Extra-scare-icular activities:
Fearleading squad.
I'm never without ...
high-voltage hair! My black-and-white
streaks are hard to miss.
I'm always saying ...
"bolts!"
My ghoulfriends say I'm ...
electrifyingly enthusiastic
and scarily stylish.

Age:
1,600
Fave subject:
Creative writing
Worst subject:
Ge-ogre-phy
GFFs:
Frankie Stein and Clawdeen Wolf
Extra-scare-icular activities:
Fearleading squad;
Newspaper Club president.
I'm never without ...
Count Fabulous™, my BFF – that's Bat
Friend Forever. Oh, and a make-up bag
full of 'Fierce & Flawless' products.
I'm always saying ...
"fangtastic!"
My ghoulfriends say I'm ...
the most fiendishly friendly
vampire around.

Clawdeen Wolf™

Age:
15
Fave subject:
Economics – I'm going to
set up my own fashion empire.
Worst subject:
Physical dead-ucation
(they won't let me wear my heels).
GFFs:
Draculaura and Frankie Stein
Extra-scare-icular activities:
Fearleading squad;
football team; track team;
Fashion Entrepreneur Club.
I'm never without …
the latest hot bag or shoes
– a ghoul can never have too
many ughsome accessories.
I'm always saying …
"clawsome!"

My ghoulfriends say I'm …
a fierce fashionista who's
loyal to the claw.

Cleo de Nile™

Age:
5,843 (give or take a few years)
Fave subject:
Geometry (it involves
pyramid shapes).
Worst subject:
History – been there, seen that!
GFFs:
Ghoulia Yelps, and
Deuce Gorgon is my boyfriend.
Extra-scare-icular activities:
Captain of the fearleading squad.

I'm never without …
my bag of cursed icons – I never
know when I might need them.
I'm always saying …
"oh my Ra!"
My ghoulfriends say I'm …
the most golden and talented
head fearleader … ever!

MONSTER HIGH

Lagoona Blue™

Age:
15
Fave subject:
Oceanography of course!
Worst subject:
Geology
GFFs:
Frankie, Clawdeen, Draculaura, Cleo,
Abbey … I'm a friendly kind of ghoul.
Extra-scare-icular activities:
Swim team captain.
I'm never without …
a tube of monsturizer – I don't
want my skin to dry up when
I'm out of the water.
I'm always saying …
"something's fishy!"
My ghoulfriends say I'm …
a creepy-calm and caring crusader.

Ghoulia Yelps™

Age:
16 (monster years)
Fave subject:
This is like asking me
to choose which one of my
zombie relatives I prefer!
I love them all equally.
Worst subject:
There is something to be learned
from every class. Even dodgeball
teaches one to duck.
GFFs:
Cleo de Nile and Spectra Vondergeist
Extra-scare-icular activities:
Comic Book Club president.
I'm never without …
my schedule – it's even synced
to my iCoffin!
I'm always saying …
"uggh ruuur!"
**My ghoulfriends
say I'm …**
frighteningly clever.

Abbey Bominable™

Spectra Vondergeist™

Age:
16
Fave subject:
Maths
Worst subject:
Drama – only kind of scene
I like is view of mountains.
GFFs:
Lagoona Blue and Frankie Stein
Extra-scare-icular activities:
Snowboarding team captain.
I'm never without ...
my ice crystal necklace – it cools
air around me so I am not
getting too hot.
I'm always saying ...
"cool it!"
My ghoulfriends say I'm ...
strong and very long – I mean
to say tall. And have warm heart
under icy touch.

Age:
16
Fave subject:
Journalism – it runs
through the places where
my veins used to be.
Worst subject:
Maths – it's never open
to interpretation.
GFFs:
Ghoulia Yelps
Extra-scare-icular activities:
Newspaper Club (weekly column
Oh My Oracle and online blog
Ghostly Gossip).
I'm never without ...
my camera and iCoffin – I don't
want to miss a monster scoop!
I'm always saying ...
"I've been waiting my entire death
to cover a story like this!"
My ghoulfriends say I'm ...
a ghostly gossip guru.

Robecca Steam™

Age:
116
Fave subject:
Metalwork
Worst subject:
Home ick – although I'm fangtastic at boiling water!
GFFs:
Rochelle Goyle and Frankie Stein
Extra-scare-icular activities:
Skultimate Roller Maze.
I'm never without ...
a set of spanners and my rocket boots, which are great for pulling scary-cool stunts.
I'm always saying ...
"full scream ahead!"
My ghoulfriends say I'm ...
the school scare-devil.

Rochelle Goyle™

Age:
415
Fave subject:
Architecture
Worst subject:
Swimming – I sink like stone.
GFFs:
Ghoulia Yelps, Robecca Steam and Venus McFlytrap
Extra-scare-icular activities:
Skultimate Roller Maze.
I'm never without ...
a book – I've loved reading ever since my family chose to protect the Monster High library.
I'm always saying ...
"travel beyond the stone you sit on."
My ghoulfriends say I'm ...
horribly hard-headed and dead-fully protective.

Venus McFlytrap ™

Age:
15
Fave subject:
Biteology
Worst subject:
Woodwork – I can hear the screams when the saw goes in.
GFFs:
Lagoona, Robecca, Rochelle, Frankie and Ghoulia
Extra-scare-icular activities:
Chairmonster of the Monster High Green Party.
I'm never without ...
my pollens of persuasion – they have a funny effect on those around me.
I'm always saying ...
"don't be a loser, be a re-user!"
My ghoulfriends say I'm ...
a loveable tree-hugger who leads by example.

Deuce Gorgon ™

Age:
16
Fave subject:
Home ick – it's the best class at Monster High.
Worst subject:
Home ick – I pretend to hate it!
BFFs:
Jackson Jekyll is my beast bud and Cleo de Nile is my ughsome ghoulfriend.
Extra-scare-icular activities:
Casketball team (guard).
I'm never without ...
my shades – otherwise it's a rockin' day at Monster High, you get me?
I'm always saying ...
"hey monster, what's up?"
My friends say I'm ...
a scary-cool skater dude with attitude.

Student Bodies

Skelita Calaveras™

Age:
15
Fave subject:
Home Ick. It's almost like
not being in class at all!
Worst subject:
Music. I couldn't carry a tune in a casket.
GFFs:
Jinafire Long and Clawdeen Wolf
Extra-scare-icular activities:
Anything associated with
Día de los Muertos.
I'm never without ...
sugar skulls! My favourite treat.
I'm always saying ...
"kindness to the bone!"
My ghoulfriends say I'm ...
always looking for
an excuse to skelebrate!

Jinafire Long™

Age:
15 hundred scales
Fave subject:
Metal Shop. I love creating
steel sculpture.
Worst subject:
Physical dead-ucation.
Sweat makes my scales itch.
GFFs:
Skelita Calaveras and Clawdeen Wolf
Extra-scare-icular activities:
Calligraphy – it helps me to relax.
I'm never without ...
my sketchbook, for new ideas.
I'm always saying ...
"the spicier the better!"
My ghoulfriends say I'm ...
... strong willed, hot tempered,
but always willing to lend a hand.

Howleen Wolf™

Age:
14

Fave subject:
I kind of like maths and sometimes hiss-tory … or biteology.

Worst subject:
It changes every day. Weird huh?

GFFs:
Abbey Bominable and Clawdeen Wolf

Extra-scare-icular activities:
I love playing soccer.
It's so much fun!

I'm never without …
Cushion™, my pet hedgehog.

I'm always saying …
"I want to howl at my own moon."

My ghoulfriends say I'm …
not just Clawdeen's little sister!

Gigi Grant™

Age:
Dad says I'm 15, but he lost my birth certificate somewhere between Darius the Great and Julius Caesar, so I'm not sure.

Fave subject:
Astronomy – I love space!

Worst subject:
Driver's Ed. The car is too small!

GFFs:
I wish I could name just a few!

Extra-scare-icular activities:
Sightseeing.

I'm never without …
some of my father's secret-recipe hummus. Yum!

I'm always saying …
"this is a wish come true!"

My ghoulfriends say I'm …
the kind of ghoul who detests being bottled up!

Student Bodies

Twyla™

Age:
15
Fave subject:
Psychology – it helps me
to make it through the night.
Worst subject:
Anything that involves
public speaking.
GFFs:
Spectra Vondergeist and Howleen Wolf
Extra-scare-icular activities:
Capturing normie nightmares.
I'm never without ...
a 'blurple' accessory.
I'm always saying ...
"be a boo-tiful dreamer!"
My ghoulfriends say I'm ...
a shadowy figure.

Honey Swamp™

Age:
115 (in swamp monster years)
Fave subject:
Cinema-togre-phy.
I love learning new tricks.
Worst subject:
Home Ick. Darlin' I already
know how to cook.
GFFs:
Viperine Gorgon and Clawdia Wolf
Extra-scare-icular activities:
I am a photographer. I do not *want* to
be one you understand I *am* one.
I'm never without ...
my camera.
I'm always saying ...
"there's always time to do it right."
My ghoulfriends say I'm ...
a perfectionist.

Age: 19

Fave subject: Philosophy of Screamplay Structure – it sounds boring but it's really creepy cool!

Worst subject: Art. I can write my ideas, but I certainly can't draw them!

GFFs: My brothers and sisters.

Extra-scare-icular activities: Writing! I write every day 'cause if you don't write, you can't call yourself a writer.

My ghoulfriends say I'm … the one with the 'clumsy gene' in our family.

Clawdia Wolf ™

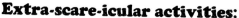

Age: 17

Fave subject: Art. Painting, sculpting and colour theory skills all come in handy when doing make-up.

Worst subject: Maths. Oh, I'm good at it, it's just not my favourite.

GFFs: Veronica von Vamp and Honey Swamp.

Extra-scare-icular activities: I love doing, shopping for and experimenting with make-up.

My ghoulfriends say I'm … a boho-chic hippie ghoul.

Viperine Gorgon ™

Age: 1,601 years old

Fave subject: Drama. I have trained with the finest acting coaches in the world

Worst subject: Physical Deaducation. I suppose it would be okay if I could use a stunt monster to take my place....

GFFs: Draculaura and Viperine Gorgon

Extra-scare-icular activities: Acting (once I've got over my stage fright).

My ghoulfriends say I'm … a natural on stage and in front of a camera.

Elissabat ™

Age: 17
Fave subject: Biteology – my long-term scareer goal is to work in sports medicine.
Worst subject: Home ick
BFFs: A pack leader never has favourites!

Extra-scare-icular activities:
Football team captain.
My friends say I'm ... furrociously athletic and surprisingly smart.

Clawd Wolf ™

Age: 16 ... in phantom years
Fave subject: Music history – music is my unlife.
Worst subject: Mad science. Sorry Mr Hack, the only thing I wanna create is scary-sweet music!

GFFs: Deuce Gorgon and Holt Hyde
Extra-scare-icular activities: Monster High Music Society member.
My ghoulfriends say I'm ... the ghoul with the unearthly voice and va-va-voom vintage style.

Operetta ™

Age: 16
Fave subject: Mad Science – guess it's in my blood.
Worst subject: Physical deaducation, especially when we play dodgeball!
BFFs: Frankie Stein and Deuce Gorgon

Extra-scare-icular activities: Monster High Music Society member.
My friends say I'm ... crazy-cool (for a normie), although scarily unreliable at times.

Jackson Jekyll

Age: 16
Fave subject: Music theory – you don't get to be the beast DJ around by luck!
Worst subject: Everything else

BFFs: I'm down with any monster who digs my beats.
Extra-scare-icular activities: Skultimate Roller Maze.
My friends say I'm ... a smokin' hot mixer.

Holt Hyde

14

Age: 16

Fave subject: Art, home ick, geometry. I can do all three at the same time and make them all work together.

Worst subject: Dead languages. I basically have to sit on my hands the entire class, which makes me anxious.

GFFs: Ghoulia Yelps and Clawdeen Wolf

Extra-scare-icular activities: I love lending helping hands to my friends by taking their ideas and bringing them to unlife with my illustration and sewing skills.

My ghoulfriends say I'm ... a fan ghoul – it's scary-cool that they trust me with their visions.

Wydowna Spider

Age: 15 – though I'm only on the first of my nine lives.

Fave subject: Drama – I can mimic other monsters purrfectly.

Worst subject: Anything which gets my purrfect paws dirty.

GFFs: Meowlody and Purrsephone

Extra-scare-icular activities: Debate team member. I adore a good argument.

My ghoulfriends say I'm ... a catty kitty who never comes when I'm called.

Toralei Stripe™

Age: 15

Fave subject: Mad science – especially the module on genetics.

Worst subject: Home ick – Ms Kindergrübber makes us wear full-body hairnets.

GFFs: Meowlody and Toralei

Extra-scare-icular activities: Gymnastics Club – we always land on our feet.

My ghoulfriends say I'm ... purrfectly identical to my sister.

Purrsephone™

Age: 15

Fave subject: Mad science – especially the module on genetics.

Worst subject: Home ick – Ms Kindergrübber makes us wear full-body hairnets.

GFFs: Purrsephone and Toralei

Extra-scare-icular activities: Gymnastics Club – we always land on our feet.

My ghoulfriends say I'm ... purrfectly identical to my sister.

Meowlody™

Student Bodies

Age: 15 years
Fave subject: Li-terror-ture – I love to lose myself in books.
Worst subject: Any class where Mr Zarr is booked as the substitute creature.

GFFs: HooDude Voodoo
Extra-scare-icular activities:
Growl Choir member.
My ghoulfriends say I'm ... friendly and wail-y helpful.

Scarah Screams ™

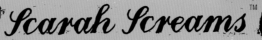

Age: 16 years
Fave subject: Swimming
Worst subject: Mad science – except when Lagoona and I get paired up for assignments!

BFFs: Deuce Gorgon and Lagoona Blue
Extra-scare-icular activities: Swim team member.
My friends say I'm ... laid-back and sensitive, but an unbeatable monster in the pool!

Gillington 'Gil' Webber ™

Age: 16 years
Fave subject: Music – I'm a keen guitar player.
Worst subject: Any class where I don't get to sit next to a scary-cute ghoul.

BFFs: Clawd Wolf, Deuce Gorgon, Gil Webber
Extra-scare-icular activities: Track team.
My friends say I'm ... the fire and soul of the party!

Heath Burns ™

Age: 17 years
Fave subject: Physical dead-ucation
Worst subject: Music – I can't stand Heath Burns' guitar playing.

BFFs: Gil Webber, Heath Burns. I have a crush on Ghoulia Yelps.
Extra-scare-icular activities: Chess Club member, casketball team member.
My friends say I'm ... deathly slow, but sorta sweet.

Sloman 'Slo Mo' Mortavitch ™

Age: Hoo knows? I'm pretty recent, but let's say 15, to make things simple.

Fave subject: Scarecology – I'd like to counsel other monsters.

Worst subject: Volcanology – unsurprising seeing as I'm made of cloth. I'm not a fan of subjects involving fire!

GFFs: Scarah Screams, Frankie Stein

Extra-scare-icular activities: Football team – I'm the tackling target.

My friends say I'm ... a grrrreat listener who can be a horrific pain – due to my voodoo flaw.

HooDude Voodoo™

We don't want to miss any student out of the Monster High Fearbook! Use the space below to add your photo and deets.

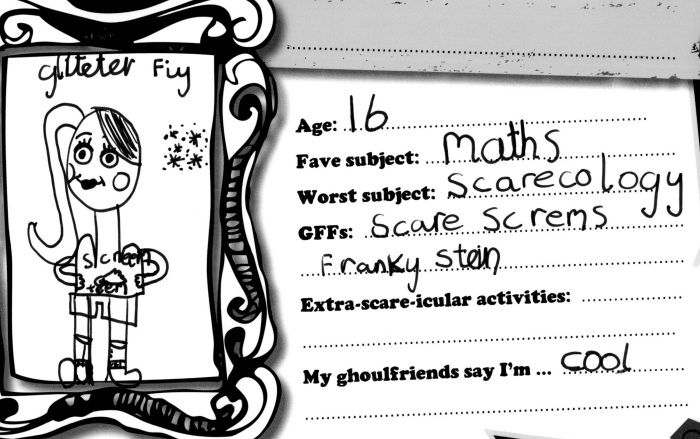

gliteter Fiy

Age: 16

Fave subject: maths

Worst subject: scarecology

GFFs: Scare screms Franky stein

Extra-scare-icular activities:

My ghoulfriends say I'm ... cool

FEARSOME FACULTY

We at Monster High are privileged to have a deadly team of academics helping to fill our skulls with knowledge. These pages are dead-icated to our fearsome faculty members.

Headless Headmistress Bloodgood
Headmistress and Trigular Calcometry 101 Teacher

Credentials:

Sleepy Hollow State B.S. Equestrian Studies
Marie Antoinette AEM M.A. Horticulture/Para-Psychology

Why we love her....

"Because she is letting me stay while I am doing my studies at the school and am being so very far away from home in the mountains. I think she is good lady."

Abbey Bominable

"She is very nice with animals, which is important for our world."
Venus McFlytrap

"Because she is a great and inspirational role model to the student bodies."
Ghoulia Yelps

Common Bloodgood-isms....

"Tally-ho Nightmare ... away!"

"Losing your head is no excuse for not doing the right thing!"

Fave Bloodgood moments

"When she let me and the girls have an overnight creepover in the school on Frightday 13th! I got to make Toralei eat furballs 'cause we made it through the night without getting spooked by the beast of coffin corridor. We threw him a totally ughsome party!"

Cleo de Nile

"When she chained me and Abbey together for the day to teach us to get along. It turned out to be a voltageous idea and now we're beast friends."

Frankie Stein

Ms Kindergrübber
Home Ick Teacher

Mr Hackington
Mad Science Teacher

Credentials:

Skinner College B.S. Chemistry
Lancet and Czechit School of Science
M.S. Taxidermy

Why we love him....

"Despite the fact that he loves to cut things up in his class, like poor little frogs – which is never cool – he's not afraid to back down under pressure from sea creatures." Lagoona Blue

Fave 'Hack' moments

"When, like, he turned up with some blood sausages during casketball – that meaty snack helped me win the game!"
Clawd Wolf

"When his 'care for an egg' assignment went horrifically wrong. The egg hatched and attacked Mr H!"
Gil Webber

Common Hack-ism....
"HEATH BURNS!!!!!
Do you want to end up in dead-tention for the rest of your life?"

Mr D'eath
Student Guidance Counsellor

Fave Mr D'eath moment

"He let me give him a monster makeover and set him up on a date. Now that's scary-cool!"
Rochelle Goyle

Credentials:

North Styx State B.A. Modern Dance/Journalism
Tombstone Tech M.A. Peace Studies

Why we love him....

"Because he's a little freaky just like us. He's got this 'regret list' where he writes down all the things he plans on regretting before the death of his soul." Frankie Stein

"He sighs a lot – but he's one fangtastically happy dude."
Deuce Gorgon

"What's the worst that could happen?"

Common D'eath-ism....

Credentials:

GGT Ghoul Graduate Trainee – retrained after formerly running 'cottage' baking industry and then running a B&B.

Why we love her....

"Because, for some reason she quite likes me – we kinda bond over my stitching." Frankie Stein

"That smells spooktacular Deuce! The rest of you ... back to the chopping board.'"

Common Grübb-ism....

Fave Kindergrübber moment

"Whεn mε and Frankiε madε a living gingεrbrεad man in hεr class. Shε lovεd thε big guy!"
Jackson Jekyll

Favourite fang-outs

Ghouls love to fang out together! Check out our spooktacular top spots.

The Maul

Where to start in the Maul? So many stores, so little time! We like to shop til we drop for scary-cool undies at Transylvania's Secret, or snap up drop-dead gorgeous pieces from Fursace, Furrberry, Jean-Maul Gaultier and Gorebana.

The creepateria

OK, so the food is mostly gruesome, but the creepateria is definitely the destination of choice for first dates, showdowns and chats with the ghouls.

Coffin corridor

Whether we're reading the latest copy of *Seventween*, swapping beauty tips or discussing hot dates, the coffin corridor is a great place to fang out. It's totes ugh-mazing what we can fit in those coffin-shaped lockers – bags full of sugared eyeballs, Fierce & Flawless products, cursed idols, plus the odd frog or 20!

Cleo's golden boudoir

Oh my Ra! Cleo's bedroom is scarily spacious. We love hanging here and playing the board game Gargoyles to Gargoyles – although everyone except Abbey lets Cleo win.

The Coffin Bean

The drinks are to die for at the Coffin Bean – they're poured by the monster world's beast barista, Lagoona Blue! We head here to rest our weary, high-heeled paws after a hard night's spend-a-thon.

The juicer

When we can't get off the school grounds to go to the Maul, the juice machine is the next best thing! Just make sure you don't go with Abbey – unless you want a smoothie frozen so hard it'll crack your fangs.

Clawdeen's clawsome cave

Clawdeen's crib is as fierce as you'd expect a werewolf's room to be. The purple colour scheme and animal print furnishings scream glamour. Her closet is so packed with ughsome outfits, her sister Howleen can't keep away!

The monster movie theatre

Deuce loves scary human films, Clawd's into action, while silent movies are more Jackson's scream. Whatever the guys wanna watch is fine with us … as long as it involves popcorn in the dark!

Draculaura's dark den

Draculaura's room is pink, black and totes adorable – just like its owner. We head there after school when we want to pamp with the vamp!

Frankie's fab lab

Frankie sleeps in the basement laboratory. It's pretty unique as bedrooms go – dark, forbidding and stacked full of crazy machines and electrical wiring – perfect for spooky creepovers.

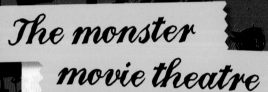

NEED A SHRINK?

I always find it ugh-mazing that students whose brains are still half empty – like caverns full of cobwebs – think they know everything! How do they expect to fool experienced teachers such as I, Mr Hackington?

During one mad science class, I was called away to deal with a dragon. I told the students to sit still and not touch the powerful and dangerous piece of technology on my desk. Of course, no sooner was I out of the room than Master Burns began to fiddle! With a flick of a switch, every student body was shrunk to the size of an ant.

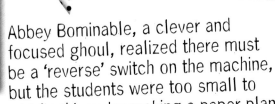

Abbey Bominable, a clever and focused ghoul, realized there must be a 'reverse' switch on the machine, but the students were too small to get to it. Flashy Burns thought he could fix things by making a paper plane and flying over to my desk. What he didn't factor in was crashing to the ground after his flaming hair set the plane on fire. All seemed lost. The class was certain I would return, find out what had happened and they would all be for the chop!

Luckily Abbey used her head. Clawd squirted liquid from a syringe towards my desk, then Abbey used her powers to freeze it into an ice bridge. The pair reached the machine and flicked the 'reverse' switch.

By the time I walked into the room everyone was sitting in their seats as if nothing had happened. The class still spent a week in dead-tention, however. Why? Because they had also managed to enlarge a spider that had been scuttling across my desk at the time. The giant arachnid gave the students away! (I made sure that it, too, got dead-tention.)

Mr Hackington

Heath Burns really cannot keep out of trouble. He was the one responsible for messing with my electromagnetic science project. He managed to short-circuit the entire school by messing with my invention. (Draculaura was supposed to be making sure no one came near, but she got an urgent call on her iCoffin and, while she wasn't looking, Heath flicked a switch). Within seconds the whole of Monster High was plunged into darkness. The air was filled with the screams of student bodies – including mine – all unable to finish our homework assignments.

Step forwards newbie Robecca Steam. Somehow the old-fashioned ghoul managed to save the day using traditional study methods. First she got the dragon in the catacombs to light candles so we could see, then she replaced Heath's computer with her typewriter. She showed Draculaura how to write with a quill and send a letter by bat, taught me how to use an abacus instead of a clawculator and even helped Clawdeen use books for research rather than the net.

I came to the conclusion that Robecca is utterly ughsome! The resourceful ghoul hoped that we might adopt her ways for good and stop trying to lend her our iCoffins, cameras and computers … but then the power came back on!

Ghoulia

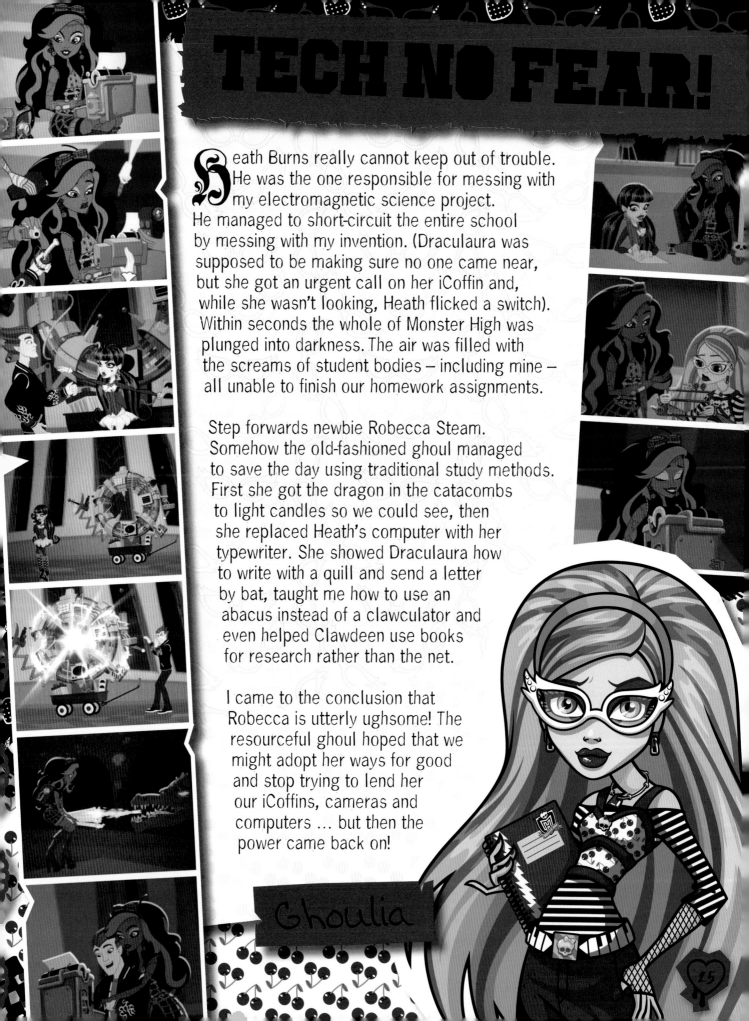

25

Abyss friends forever

The beast thing about unlife at school is the monsters. I have the best ghoulfriends in the whole world and know they will always go that extra mile for me – or swim that extra fathom! That's what happened when Frankie asked to borrow the scary-gorgeous necklace that Clawd had given me. Of course I said yes straight away. We love swapping outfits and I had borrowed a pair of her killer heels only the week before!

As Frankie put the necklace on, she accidentally touched both her bolts. The shock sent the bling flying into … the deep end of the pool! Frankie is such a newbie, I had to explain to her that no one goes in the deep end, EVER! The pool is the deepest in the world – no one knows what lurks at the bottom.

Frankie being Frankie insisted on climbing into a deep-sea diving suit. Before I could say 'blundering bats' she was in the pool with Lagoona, who's like the best swimmer in the whole of Monster High! The ghouls dodged lots of scary creatures down there, before finding my necklace in a cave guarded by a giant squid. The naughty beast was hoarding a whole stack of other treasures that had fallen in the water over the years. Frankie shocked the squid into returning everything – from my necklace to Jackson's fave T97X4 clawculator. My fearsome friends did the whole school a favour that day!

Draculaura

NO SUBSTITUTE FOR GOOD LISTENING

Some teachers at Monster High are pretty ughsome! I personally kinda like Ms Kindergrübber, though I'd never admit in public that my favourite class is home ick.

Anyhow, among all the brilliantly talon-ted faculty members there is one horrible exception – Mr Lou Zarr, the substitute creature. I imagine the first time we met will stick with him forever. I came in late to class (which, granted, is pretty annoying) but it couldn't be avoided 'cause I was totally getting changed after casketball practice. Mr Zarr got razzed. I don't think it helped after he said, "You're late," and I replied, "Nah, I'm Deuce, Deuce Gorgon!" He then told me to take off my shades. Baaaad move – so, so bad!

I tried to tell Mr Zarr, but he wouldn't listen. Even when all the other monsters in class covered their faces with books, he didn't get it. So I took my glasses off and … whaddya know? There was a new statue at Monster High. Loser in stone! What? Oh sorry, make that 'Lou Zarr' in stone!

DEUCE

Horror stories

Truth or scare

I've only just joined Monster High, but everyone here is fiendishly friendly. I can't wait to be invited to one of the ghouls' famous slumber parties. The last one sounded scary-cool!

On the night of the party, all of the ghouls rocked up to Clawdeen's lair to fang out and chat. Frankie was totes freaked after reading in *Monsterbeat* magazine about the game 'truth or scare' where GFFs choose either a dare or to tell a shocking secret.

Frankie didn't like the idea of telling Cleo the truth about which boy she was crushing on, so she tried a heap of stalling tactics to avoid playing the game. But crafty Cleo wouldn't let it drop. She scared Frankie to send a text to all the boys at Monster High saying, 'Party at my house – spread the word'.

Cleo couldn't believe it when Frankie actually plucked up the courage to send the text. "Your parents are going to freak when all those boys turn up at your house!" she cackled.

The joke was on Cleo when she discovered that Frankie had sent the text from *her* iCoffin! The boys were stampeding round to Cleo's as they spoke! Spookily enough, that was the last time Miss de Nile suggested a game of truth or scare!

Rochelle

Lagoona's Aunt Lantic

My ghoulfriend Lagoona's a straight A student. If only my parents would meet her they'd discover how bright and intelligent she is, sigh!

Being super-smart, Lagoona freaked out when one of her teachers asked to see her parents to discuss her work. She just couldn't understand it! The sitch got worse when Clawdeen told her that she must have totally failed. My poor salty was beside her fins with anxiety!

That's when Clawdeen came up with possibly her most bizarre idea ever. She suggested dressing someone up as one of Lagoona's family so her folks wouldn't find out that she'd failed. The question was who? Slo Mo happened to be slouching nearby. Before he could say "Uuugggrrhh!", he was being made up to look like Lagoona's fake 'Aunt Lantic'.

Mo looked truly ugh-ful, but he went in to see the teacher anyway. Everyone waited on tenter-claws outside. Luckily the plan ran like a nightmare. Not only was the teacher fooled, he also explained that he wanted to see Lagoona's folks to tell them that she'd written her best ever essay.

I was so proud of Lagoona. Now I just have to convince my folks that she's the best thing since sliced pondweed!

Gil

monstrous
MEMORIES

What's your favourite Monster High moment? Here's a collection of our most cherished paw-sonal memories....

"Where to start? I have been solely responsible for so many ugh-mazing moments this year. Getting us invited to Gloom Beach, winning the Spirit Staff, triumphing at the Mashionals! Oh, and sticking it to Nefera, sister of doom!" Cleo

"It was pretty incredible working with Frankie on our life-sized gingerbread guy for home ick. Doing anything with Frankie is ugh-mazing!" Jackson

"Rewiring Hoodude's brain to give him more confidence. You don't get to do that often!" Scarah

"I enjoyed the power cut caused by Heath Burns which meant that all technology died at Monster High! For one day I got to show the student bodies how they could exist without their iCoffins, tablets and clawculators!" Robecca

"I loved working with that fine monster, Deuce, on a song for his ghoulfriend. The chance to write for someone who appreciates my little ol' style of music cancelled out the stress of dealin' with that total pain, Cleo." Operetta

"When Frankie got everyone — including me — tickets to see Justin Biter in concert! She's the beast GFF ever!" Ghoulia

"I remember when the ghouls tried to make me feeling not so much home sick by locking me into freezer. Was very kindness to me. Almost making me to cry." Abbey

"WATCHING JACKSON JEKYLL CHANGE INTO HOLT HYDE FOR THE FIRST TIME. HILARIOUS! AND GETTING A DATE WITH DRACULAURA, YEAH, THOSE ARE MY TWO TOP MEMORIES THIS YEAR." Heath

"My favourite memory was when the ghouls dressed Slo Mo up as my aunt to attend the Parent-Creature Conference. He looked bonzer! There were no worries anyhow because the teacher just wanted to talk about my excellent grades!" Lagoona

"When Clawdeen and Clawd thought that I believed all of Clawdia's stories were true! The whole school knows she's a fur-rociously creative writer!" Howleen

"It was totes amazing when our GFFs planned a surprise joint party for Draculaura and me. It was my Sweet 16 days and her Sweet 1,600 years! We had both been trying to sort out a party for each other, but no one could come, because they were all planning a joint party for us both!" Frankie

"UUUUGGHHG!"

(Ghoulia led our zombie team to victory at dodgeball by using her trigular calcometry skills.) Slo Mo

"I loved it when Emily Anne came to school for Monster High's "We Stop Hate" campaign. She spread so much love, love, love!" Draculaura

"WHEN THE ZOMBIES WERE FIGHTING OVER GHOULIA YELPS! I'VE SEEN PAINT DRY FASTER!" Holt

Abbey Bominable's
QUOTES OF THE YEAR

Unlike we mountain-dwelling monsters who are not into the small talk, the Monster High student bodies love to be doing chat together. Here are some of the best sound bites I have heard when fanging out in the howlways.

"I didn't have time to study. I got busy. You think these pores just shrink themselves?"
Draculaura

"Knowledge is the cure for every curse."
Mr Hack

"YOU LOOK HORRIBLE! I LIKE THAT IN A GIRL!"
Heath

"No way am I going out with a guy with more than four eyes ... and he has like, eight!" Frankie

"I nailed the finals like a coffin, sista!"
Clawdeen

"Woah! Slow ya growls."
Clawd

"Holt Hyde? No, I don't know him."
Jackson

"Draculaura, you're pretty pumped for somebody without a pulse!" Cleo

"WHO YOU CALLIN' A BULL?" Manny

32

"Cleo's been working that cursed idol like a credit card with no limit!" Clawdeen

"MONSTER HIGH'S ABOUT BEING COOL TO EVERYONE NO MATTER WHO OR WHAT YOU ARE, EVEN IF THAT MEANS A "NORMIE." Deuce

"It might come back to bite ya!" Lagoona

"If I don't get a scoop soon, I'm just gonna live!" Spectra

"I don't mind when people talk about me. It's when they stop talking about you that you have to worry." Nefera

"I couldn't study for the SATS, my brother ate all my notes." Clawdeen

"I just want to crawl into a puddle and pull it over the top of me!" Lagoona

"She does so much for me I thought I should do something nice for her. But don't tell anyone — it'll totally ruin my rep." Cleo

"Let's just say my clothes aren't the only thing that's fierce during a full moon!" Clawdeen

"I've known Clawd since before he was housebroken." Draculaura

"Y'all are pickin' on the wrong fiddle." Operetta

"Uuuughrrrghgghghugh." Ghoulia

"No one is to look directly at me unless it's in amazement." Cleo

"I DON'T GIVE AS!" Mr Rotter

"You are one misdeed away from the study howl of eternal homework – oh, and fiery demons will descend upon your house." Headmistress Bloodgood

"Voltageous fail! It was like I had death breath." Frankie

"DO YOU BELIEVE IN LOVE AT FIRST FRIGHT? OR SHOULD I WALK BY AGAIN?" Heath

"we find out who runs things and we show them who's boss. Then we ghouls will run the school." Toralei

33

CLUBS

Fashion Entrepreneurs' Club

The main event in the club's calendar was the Fashion Talon Show, part of the 1,361st annual Fashion Show. The event was a howling success due to the jaw-dropping performance of Clawdeen Wolf. The fierce fashionista put on a catwalk show to make flesh crawl and fur stand on end, strutting her stuff in her own designs like a true professional. It's not known what caused the changes to Clawdeen's routine, but the spotlights in the room may have replicated the effect of a full moon.

1361st ANNUAL CHARITY FASHION SHOW

NEWSPAPER CLUB

Monster High's Newspaper Club has benefited from the hard work and enthusiasm of two particular members this year. Budding photographer Draculaura has captured some of the school's standout moments on camera for the front page. The gossip section has also been dripping with gory details thanks to journalist-in-the-making, Spectra Vondergeist. It's all part of keeping every student body up to date on the latest hauntings and happenings at Monster High.

DEBATE TEAM

Mr Where's Debate Team has enjoyed a howlingly fulfilled year at the rostrum. Subjects up for debate have included 'Monsters and the wider world' and 'To devour or not to devour?' The team welcomed new member Venus McFlytrap, who has a particular interest in ecological matters. Miss McFlytrap is eager for her voice to be heard.

CLUBS

Comic Book Club

Comic Book Club president, Ghoulia Yelps, is as dead-icated a collector as she is an illustrator. This year, the school even enjoyed an exhibition of some of her work! Her personal highlight was the surprising acquisition of the ultra-rare first edition of the *Deadfast* comic. The precious mag was given to her by an unlikely and extremely generous benefactor.

Ghoulia sketching her comic book hero.

CHESS CLUB

Chess has proved the perfect hobby for Slo Mo. The lumbering zombie is blazing a trail through both intra and inter-school competitions. Zombies excel at chess, due to the pace of the game and the logic required. Fellow club member and Mo appreciator, Ghoulia Yelps, writes, "We fully expect him to achieve Growl Master status."

GO MO!

Growl Choir

It has been a time of consolidation and hard graft for the choir as they attempt to make the grade for next year's Growl Choir Of The Year contest. There was, however, a major set back mid-term when the choirmaster got sucked through a broken window during practice. The window pane shattered when Cleo de Nile's scream reverberated around the school after her squad's initial rejection from the Gloom Beach Fearleading Championships. Luckily the master has since made an almost full recovery and can now see through both eyes again.

Terrifying TRIPS

Monte Scarlo

What goes on tour, scares on tour! Let's go out and about with the Monster High student bodies....

Budgetary issues meant that the proposed visit to Scaris was cancelled, but the fangtastic Monte Scarlo trip did go ahead as planned, despite an uncertain beginning. Prior to departure, Frankie Stein came down with a hideous virus with Clawdeen, Draculaura and Cleo de Nile all getting infected. Luckily the trip was saved by exchange student Abbey Bominable! The bold ghoul braved the catacombs to find the antidote, monster thistle, despite being allergic herself. It's just another example of how fiendishly friendly student bodies can be!

FRANKIE SNEEZED FIRST

EVEN DRACULAURA AND CLEO BROKE OUT IN A RASH!

ALL SET FOR MONTE SCARLO

CLAWDEEN GOT SICK, TOO

WITHOUT ABBEY, THE TRIP WOULD HAVE BEEN A DEAD LOSS

Mad Science Fair

THE FAIR

Student bodies from Monster High enjoyed an educational day out of class at the school's Mad Science Fair. Amid the many, many entries from monstrous schools up and down the country, Cleo de Nile's amazing project stood out. Her machine to turn trash into green fuel bagged her first prize from Headmistress Bloodgood.

ANOTHER INTERESTING ENTRY

Gloom Beach

READY TO GO

HEATH BURNS SUPPLIED
THE TUNES

THE BUS

SOME RARE TIME OFF
FOR THE FEAR SQUAD

THE GANG PLAY
WATER POLO

SPIRIT STAFF FOR
MONSTER HIGH

Spirits were high on the bus to Gloom Beach this year – despite Heath Burns' non-stop guitar playing! The student bodies couldn't wait to let their fur down and soak up the spring sun.

The trip promised more work than play for Monster High's fear squad. The ghouls were based on the South Beach in order to take part in a fearleading camp and competition. Scary Murphy put the squad through their paces every single day. The hard work paid off – the ghouls brought the winners' Spirit Staff back to Monster High!

THE WINNING
ASSIGNMENT

CLEO'S
~~GHOULIA'S~~ PROJECT

CLEO GETS
THE TROPHY

The Paw-fect

I am suggesting that all student bodies find a study buddy with whom to exchange knowledge. Try my logical and geometrical diagram to help you find the paw-fect partner with whom to work. Good luck.

Who's your ultimate homework fiend? Answer each question, then follow the arrows to find your scarylicious study buddy.

My pencil case is always freaky-fabulous!

YES

Of course I'll study ... after fearleading!

YES

Hiss-tory is the best subject on the scare-iculum.

YES

NO

NO

NO

YES

YES

YE'

NO

Frankie Stein

Freaky-fab minds think alike and Frankie is one enthusiastic study buddy! When you've finished comparing scary-cool stationery, you'll get straight down to work on your hiss-tory or home ick assignments.

Cleo de Nile

Your working partnership with Cleo is sure to be golden. You'd both rather be fearleading than studying, but you'll happily swot up on geometry over a spookaccino at the Coffin Bean!

Draculaura

Even books need makeovers sometimes and, like Draculaura, you spend almost as much time on presentation as content, covering textbooks in fierce paper and highlighting passages in hot-pink pen.

40

Study Buddy

Learning is much fiercer with a study buddy.

YES

NO

I'd rather study at the Coffin Bean.

The lie-bury is the beast place to work!

I love scary-cool highlighter pens in ice-blue or pink.

YES

NO

I'd just die if my grades slipped!

Talking work through with ghoulfriends helps me revise.

YES

NO

When it comes to learning, I'm a high-tech kinda ghoul.

YES

NO

NO

YES

NO

Abbey Bominable

You and Abbey are ghouls of few words, preferring to read and write rather than discuss and recite lessons. You are both logical creatures who shine at maths and are top of Mr Mummy's class.

Ghoula Yelps

An ogre-achiever like you should definitely buddy up with Ghoulia. Just like the clever zombie you're happiest reading tomes in the lie-bury or researching your next assignment on Boo-gle.

Robecca Steam

You like to work the traditional way and would rather hand write homework with a quill than use a computer. This is long-winded, but as Robecca always says, "Less monster haste – more spooky speed!"

41

Welcome to the student lounge. We fang out here after school and between lessons. You might catch us playing terror-tennis or chillaxing with the back issues of *Teen Scream*. Check out our photo board – it's freaky-fab!

HELPING HANDS

At Monster High, we student bodies pride ourselves on always lending a hand – literally, in my case – to a fiend in need. We'd do anything for our boos! Here are some examples of the totally voltage ways we've been there for each other.

Invisi Billy helped stone-footed Rochelle Goyle land a part as the lead dancer in Mr Where's recital. He lifted her in the air to make it look as if she were leaping gracefully!

I helped calm Ghoulia's nerves by offering to be her wing-ghoul for her first date with Slo Mo.

Operetta was glad to help Deuce write a love song for Cleo.

Jinafire helped Deuce, Jackson, Manny and Heath get their casketball back from a well in the dungeons – and helped them understand that problems can't always be solved by brute force.

I helped the poor zombies get a voice in school by standing up for Slo Mo. I even got him elected Student Disembodied President!

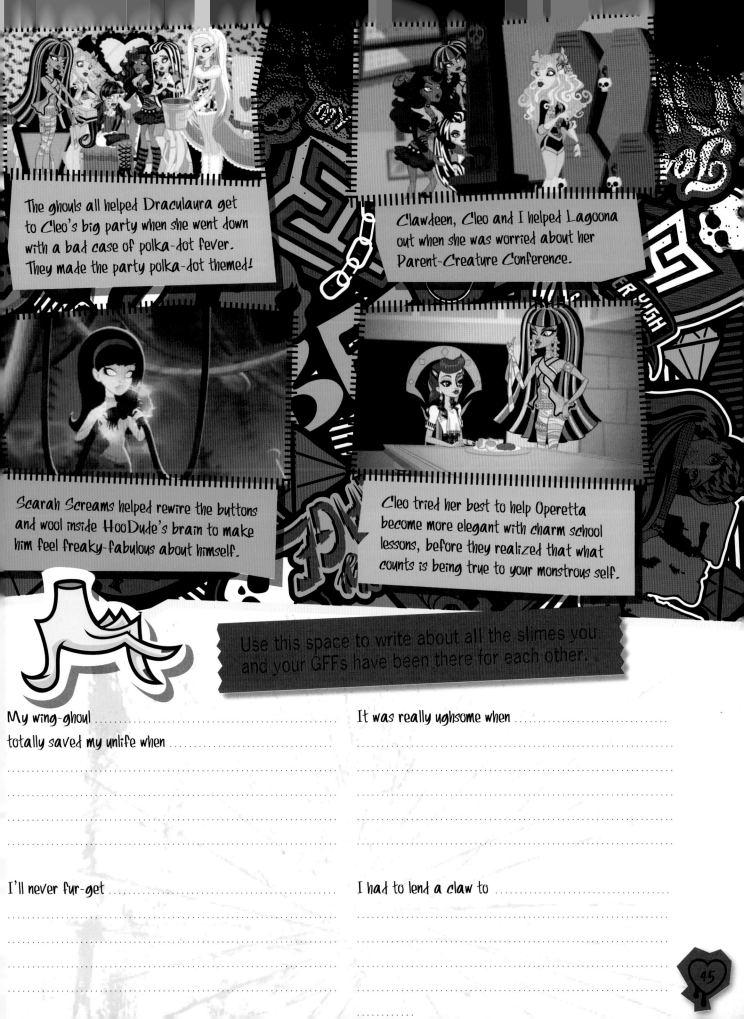

The ghouls all helped Draculaura get to Cleo's big party when she went down with a bad case of polka-dot fever. They made the party polka-dot themed!

Clawdeen, Cleo and I helped Lagoona out when she was worried about her Parent-Creature Conference.

Scarah Screams helped rewire the buttons and wool inside HooDude's brain to make him feel freaky-fabulous about himself.

Cleo tried her best to help Operetta become more elegant with charm school lessons, before they realized that what counts is being true to your monstrous self.

Use this space to write about all the slimes you and your GFFs have been there for each other.

My wing-ghoul ....
totally saved my unlife when ....
....
....
....
....

I'll never fur-get ....
....
....
....
....

It was really ughsome when ....
....
....
....
....

I had to lend a claw to ....
....
....
....
....

PICTURE DAY PICK

Picture Day is one of the most important events in the Monster High school calendar! Each student's monstrous image is preserved for eternity (and even shown in the Fearbook), so you need to look your absolute beast. Answer YES or NO to the first question, then follow the arrows through the chart to discover whose scary-cool style you'd pick to pose in.

START

I always put on my spookiest smile for the camera.

I like to check my freaky reflection before I pose.

I love electrifying patterns and prints.

YES

YES

NO

NO

NO

In a gruesome group shot, I make sure I'm at the front.

NO

A golden ghoul like me always flings on the bling.

NO

I look fierce in frills.

YES

YES

YES

YES

NO

My killer style features lots of fitted pieces.

NO

Halter neck styles look clawsome on me.

YES

I look creepily chic in mini-dresses.

YES

NO

YES

YES

NO

Plaid detail s are frightfully

I might wear shocking stockings or tights.

YES

Shoes? Hmm ... monstrous metallics are my fave.

NO

NO

Any killer h rules as lon it's black or

YES

46

A semi-up hair-do looks hairrific.

YES

YES

NO

I'm freakily unique in quirky accessories like braces.

YES

NO

NO

YES

NO

I like shoe straps that snake eerily round my ankles.

NO

Scary-cute bunches work for me.

YES

YES

NO

NO

My hair looks spooktacular worn long with a fringe.

NO

YES

You wear high-voltage heels and spooky separates to mix up a freaky-unique style that's all your own. Ughsome accessories are your thing – you know how to wear a scary-cute bag, horrific hat or beastly braces to set off your outfit. You're one fierce fashionista whose stand-out style means you always shine in the shot.

You'd die for Frankie's voltageous fashion flair!

Your spooky sweet smile looks great in photos and your colour of choice – shocking pink – always makes an impact. For a freaky photo session you match monstrous make-up with a pair of killer heels. Dresses with fierce frills make you feel gorgeously ghoul-ie.

You think Draculaura's look is fangtastic!

You know the creepy camera loves you and you're confident that you always look ugh-mazing. For your close-up you'll be wearing something fitted to show off your fearsome figure. You like wearing your hair lusciously long and spooktacularly sleek.

You admire Cleo's killer style!

Summer Snaps

PAGES 49-80

PAGE 82

PAGES 92-93

PAGES 110-111

PAGE 90

PAGE 102

PAGES 118-119

PAGE 134

© 2014 Mattel

TRUE   TRUE

FALSE   FALSE

     TRUE

FALSE   FALSE

TRUE   TRUE

FALSE   FALSE

TRUE   TRUE

FALSE   FALSE

TRUE   TRUE

     FALSE

FALSE

PAGE 152

PAGES 160-161

PAGE 162

PAGE 135

PAGE 173

MONSTER STICKER dressing

49

SPOOKY STYLES

The ghouls and guys at Monster High have cool control of their unique killer style. **Clawdeen Wolf** makes monsters howl with her fierce animal prints and **Frankie Stein's** electrifying style is totally voltage! Learn more about the monsters' freaky-fab fashion sense, then dress them in ugh-mazing outfits. You can style each monster more than once, so get creepy and get creative!

USE YOUR SCARY-COOL STICKERS AND CREEPIEST COLOURING PENS TO DRESS THE MONSTERS.

Draculaura loves to splash her black outfits with pink.

She carries a frilly umbrella to protect her vampire skin from the sun!

Cleo de Nile is a tru ancient Egyptian princess complete with bandages.

She always wears golden jewellery and is rarely seer without her iCoffin.

Frankie Stein always chooses electrifying patterned prints.

She accessorizes spookily well.

Ghoulia Yelps is never without a pair of geek-chic glasses.

She thinks the colour red is to die (again) for!

Clawdeen Wolf howls for anything purple.

She wears a wild green wig for monster parties!

51

SPOOKY STYLES

Deuce Gorgon has to wear sunglasses to keep from turning his friends to stone.

Lagoona Blue likes to creep out in her baggies, tank top and floppies.

She adds scary sparkle with her shell jewellery.

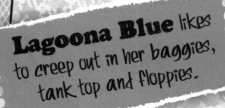

He wears scary-cool shorts and a vest for sports.

Of corpse **Cleo** always looks perfect.

Draculaura has no reflection — she relies on her ghoulfriends to tell her she looks fangtastic!

Lagoona's favourite
colour is ocean blue.

Frankie loves to accessorize with an electrifying tie.

Ghoulia loves to lurch around in blood-red clothes.

Animal prints make **Clawdeen** howl!

This ancient Egyptian princess looks ghoulish in gold.

59

Deuce keeps it creepily casual when he's shooting some hoops.

This romantic vampire loves to accessorize with lace and hearts.

Lagoona likes to dress for any kind of scary fun, like beach volleyball!

Tartan patterns make **Frankie's** bolts spark!

Being ghoulishly geeky is part of **Ghoulia's** scary-cool style.

Clawdeen's confidence makes her a fierce fashionista.

Cleo wouldn't be seen undead without royal jewellery to match her outfit.

Deuce mixes black, white and grey with bright colours that rock!

67

Draculaura is 1,600 years young, so she's had plenty of time to perfect her killer style.

Lagoona loves to dress up in a little black dress for monster parties.

69

Even when **Frankie** comes apart at the seams, her style stays perfectly in place.

Ghoulia's horn-rimmed glasses match every outfit!

Clawdeen loves purple and gold as a creeperific combination.

Cleo is technically over 5,800 years old. If she didn't wear bandages, her age would start to show!

Deuce designs his own shoes with deadly cool details.

This vegetarian vamp adds sweet details with dots and stripes.

This stylish sea monster loves to use hints of light pink that look sweet against her blue skin.

Frankie sticks to a classic look, but gives it a terrifying twist!

77

Ghoulia loves
freaky-fab T-shirts
with zombie comic-book
heroes on them.

This wildly stylish ghoul plans to start her own fierce fashion label.

Turquoise and ghoulish gold are **Cleo's** favourite colours.

UGHSOME
ACTIVITIES

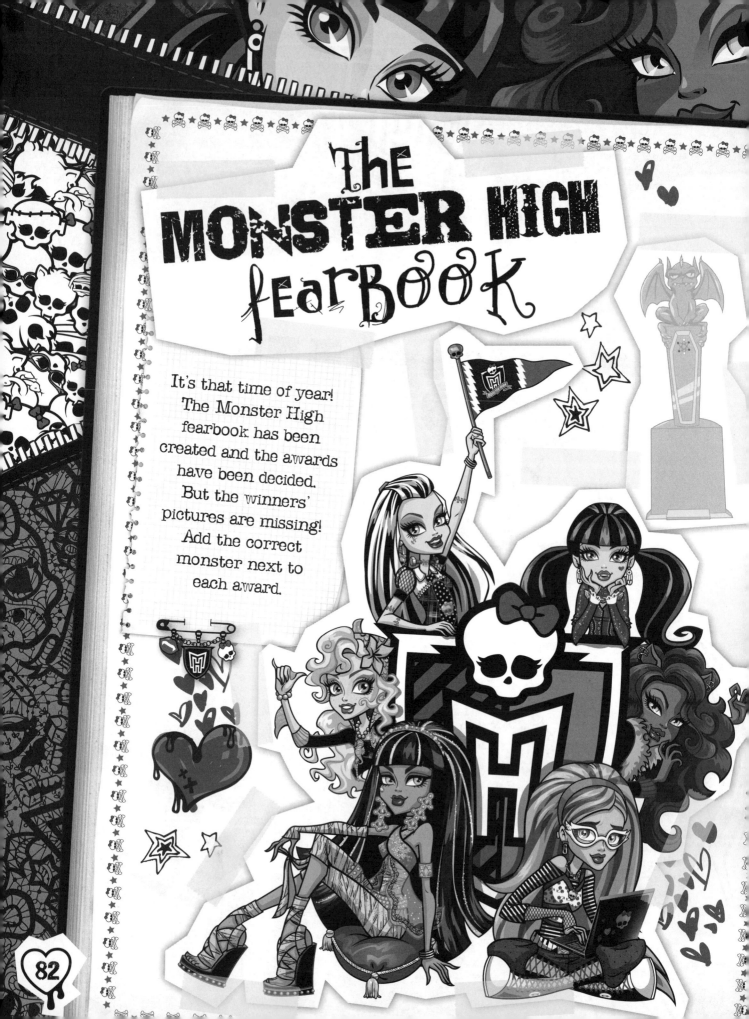

The MONSTER HIGH fearbook

It's that time of year! The Monster High fearbook has been created and the awards have been decided. But the winners' pictures are missing! Add the correct monster next to each award.

MOST LIKELY TO ...

... be an A-list star of stage and scream.

MOST LIKELY TO ...

... help out a ghoulfriend in need.

MOST LIKELY TO ...

... fly off into the sunset with the monster of her nightmares.

MOST LIKELY TO ...

... design a fur-rocious pair of killer heels.

MOST LIKELY TO ...

... go on a fangtastic round-the-world trip.

MOST LIKELY TO ...

... be the next spookily smart headmistress of Monster High.

MOST LIKELY TO ...

... become a Skultimate Roller Maze commentator.

PYRAMID PUZZLE

Help **CLEO** complete this ancient puzzle by filling in the missing numbers in the pyramid. Each gold statue should contain the total of the two numbers just below it!

20 28

7

1 2 4

84

ANSWERS ON PAGE 174

aLL MIXED up

ABBEY BOMINABLE is from the mountains and her first language is Yetish, so sometimes she gets things mixed up.

Can you help her unscramble the letters of these monsters' names? Then draw lines to match the names to the right ghouls.

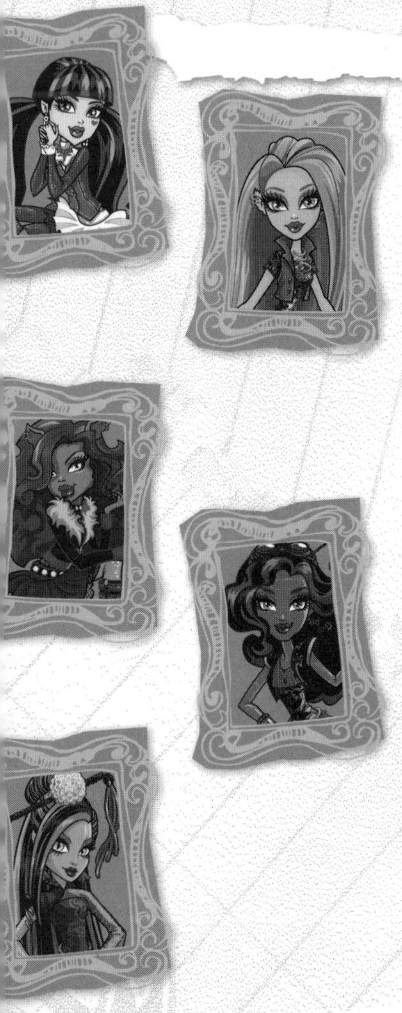

RCAUDRAAUL

CCAOREB TEMAS

REJIFINA OLGN

NUSVE YCRAFLMTP

ACEELDNW LOWF

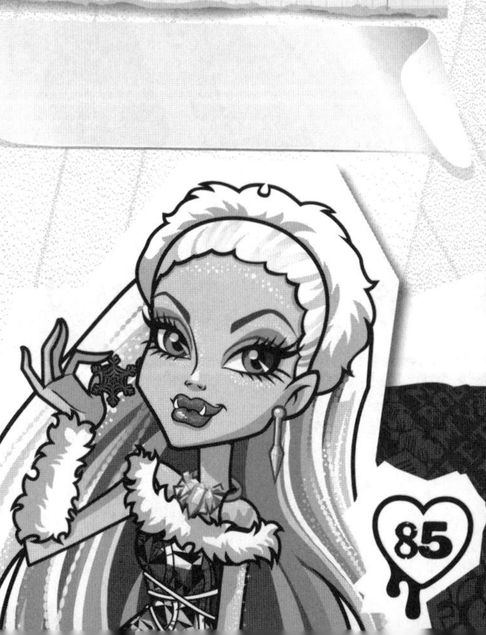

THE SQUEAL of fortUNE

FRANKIE needs a date for the Homecoming Dance and she's using the Squeal of Fortune to decide who to ask. Starting with the letter at the top of the wheel, write down every alternate letter to find out what the wheel is telling her!

ANSWER:

_ _ _ _ _ _ _ _ _ _

86

The SKELETON Crew

ANSWERS ON PAGE 174

It's the Monster High crew! Can you spot eight differences in the second picture?

87

ANSWERS ON PAGE 174

McFLYTRAP'S MISSION

VENUS McFLYTRAP is on a crusade to clean u[p] the environment. Here are some words th[at] are really important to her - and to all of u[s]. Can you find the words in the grid?

- RECYCLE
- POLLEN
- REUSE
- COMPOST
- RENEW
- TREES
- PLANTS
- AIR
- ENVIRONMENT

"WE ALL W[IN] WHEN YOU CHOOSE T[HE] RIGHT BIN!"

THE ODD COUPLE

DEUCE and CLEO are the ghoulest couple in school - she's drop-dead gore-geous and he's a cold-blooded hottie. But one of these pictures is not the same as the rest. Which one?

a

b

c

d

ANSWER: C

89

Oh my ORACLE!

Here are some letters to Spectra's advice column. Can you respond, **SPECTRA-STYLE?**

Can you guess the writers? Stick their faces next to their letters.

Dear Oracle,
I know it sounds freaky, but I really like this normie. He's sweet and kind and handsome. I think he likes me, but whenever we go on a date, he disappears. What's wrong with me?

Dear ...

Dear Oracle,
Oh. my. Ra! You've got to help me! My sister is driving me crazy! She's so beautiful on the outside but so ugly on the inside. She's threatening to tell my dad about a party I had while he was away and now I'm practically her slave. What can I do?

Dear ...

Dear Oracle,
Why won't my vampire girlfriend come near me? I won a pizza-eating contest just to impress her (and the pizza was clawsome — loads of garlic and cheese!), but afterwards she couldn't bear to be near me. Is she dumping me because I eat like a wolf?

Dear ...

CATACOMB MaZE

ANSWER ON PAGE 174

Scare-devil **ROBECCA STEAM** is practising Skultimate Roller Maze speed-skating in the catacombs. But she's been separated from Captain Penny™. Can you help Robecca take the right path to find her pet?

START

FINISH

91

FREAKY pets

All the Monster High students have ugh-mazing monster pets. Find the stickers that match the blank shapes to reunite the ghouls with their beast friends.

COUNT FABULOUS

They love fanging out together!

WATZIT

Stitched together and scary cute!

CRESCENT

Fur-ociously fuzzy and totally clawsome.

HISSETTE

Her hiss is worse
than her bite.

NEPTUNA

A fangtastic fishy friend.

SIR HOOTS-A-LOT

A wise companion,
but he doesn't do errands.

93

My SPOOKY Scare-itage

This is Mr Rotter's classroom. Check out the 'My Spooky Scare-itage' project his students are working on. Fang-scinating stuff! Some of the ghouls haven't quite finished. Shall we lend them a claw?

Be a good ghoulfriend and help the students complete their assignments on time. Read each piece of work, then fill in the blanks. All of the words you need are jumbled up in the panel opposite.

My Spooky Scare-itage

NAME: Skelita

DEAD-SCENDED FROM: Los Eskeletos

SCARY-COOL COUNTRY: ....

MY SCARE-ITAGE: I am very proud of my scare-itage and its legends and traditions. My favourite custom is Día de los .... (or Day of the Dead), where we honour our ancestors. We spend time with la familia, hold parties and decorate our homes with marigold flowers and screamily scrummy sugar skulls.

My Spooky Scare-itage

NAME: .... Long

DEAD-SCENDED FROM: Chinese ....

SCARY-COOL COUNTRY: China

MY SCARE-ITAGE: The country of my fore-monsters is very eek-xotic with customs and traditions that have carried on for thousands and thousands of years. Monsters like me were often found guarding temples. We have always had great powers and can control elements including ...., wind and water.

My Spooky Scare-itage

NAME: Cleo ...... Nile

DEAD-SCENDED FROM: ....

SCARY-COOL COUNTRY: ....

MY SCARE-ITAGE: My father tells me that, traditionally, monsters like me were entombed in pyramids in the middle of the desert with .... and gold and sooo much bling. We still live in my father's pyramid and I have my own totes amazing crypt! Our bodies were wrapped in an OTT amount of bandages — the updated version of this look we now call body-con.

MY SPOOKY SCARE-ITAGE

NAME: ....

DEAD-SCENDED FROM: The Gargoyles

SCARY-COOL CITY: ....

MY SCARE-ITAGE: Stone is a big part of my culture. My ancestors have always been found on and around great ...., such as castles and cathedrals, which we protect. Although I come from Scaris, monsters like me are found in many countries, including ancient Egypt and Greece. We can take many forms.

THE MUMMY   SCARIS   HEXICO   JINAFIRE   FIRE

DRAGONS   DE   MUERTOS   CALAVERAS

BUILDINGS   JEWELS   ROCHELLE   EGYPT   GOYLE

MY SPOOKY SCARE-ITAGE

Complete your own assignment here!

NAME: ....

DEAD-SCENDED FROM: ....

SCARY-COOL COUNTRY: ....

MY SCARE-ITAGE: ....

Voltage Vampitheatre

Mr Where's drama class takes place here, in the vampitheatre. He has been named as *Stage and Scream Magazine's* 'Deadliest Drama King' three years in a row!

Clawdeen has landed the top role in the school production of *A Monster for All Seasons*. She and Cleo de Nile always have their claws out over the leading roles!

It's time for Clawdeen's costume fitting. Design a spooktacular outfit for her to wear. This star won't go on stage looking anything less than ugh-mazing!

Li-terror-ture

I love this class! Don't you just adore the classics such as Scram Screamer's *Dracula* and my personal favourite, *Freakenstein* by Scary Shelley? The professor's away today so the supply creature Mr Lou Zarr (snigger) has asked the class to write poetry about the monster sitting next to them.

Oh my ghoul! Who are these mischievous monsters describing? Maybe you can guess.... Read the odorous odes out loud, then write in the titles.

....

by Abbey Bominable

He's a loud-mouthed flirt,
He's kind of lame,
He gets uptight,
Then bursts in flame!
The End

2

....

by Jackson Jekyll™

HER GHOULISH GAZE, EYES BLUE AND GREEN,
SPARKS THAT SPIT FROM EVERY SEAM,
OH IF SHE COULD ONLY SEE
HOW MUCH SHE MEANS TO 'NORMIE' ME.
SHE'S HELPED ME AND MY EGO 'HOLT',
WITH EVERY AMP AND EVERY VOLT
OF HER SPOOKTASTIC MONSTER SELF,
BUT I'M STILL SITTING ON THE SHELF.

....

by Operetta

Oh whatta ghoul,
This chick's so cool,
The greenest monster
In our school,
Li'l Lagoona is her pal —
guess she digs this caring gal.

4

....

by Draculaura
He's a hunky casketball star,
And I know he's gonna go far.
Even though his favourite treat,
Is pizza topped with meat,
He's still my favourite guy —
The heart never lies!

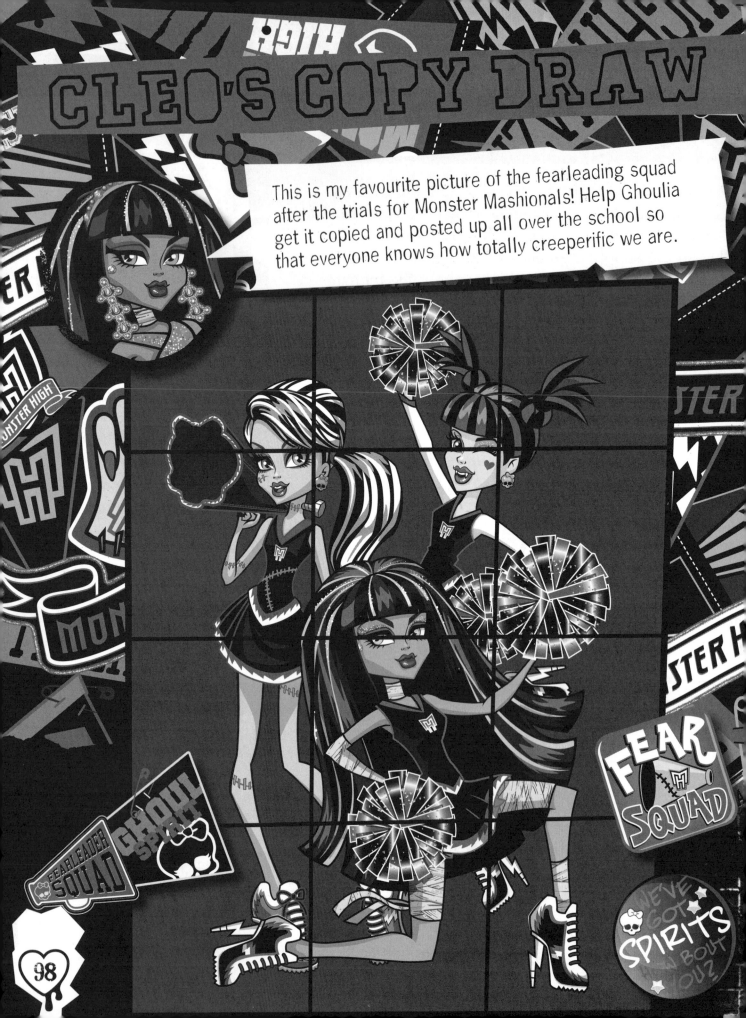

CLEO'S COPY DRAW

This is my favourite picture of the fearleading squad after the trials for Monster Mashionals! Help Ghoulia get it copied and posted up all over the school so that everyone knows how totally creeperific we are.

98

Are you ready to get scribbling? The best way to get your picture eek-xactly right is to copy each square into the blank one on this page. When you've finished drawing, colour the picture in.

ANSWERS ON PAGE 174

DEAD-TENTION

Mr Rotter has sentenced these student bodies to dead-tention, but they can't for the unlife of them work out what they've done wrong. Can you help them by matching up the monster with the crime?

DATE:

A "I guess I might have accidentally cursed my pizza with an idol and brought it to life."

B "I sneezed in the corridor and electrocuted three student bodies!"

C "I set free the poor innocent froggies that Mr Hackington was going to dissect. I had to save them!"

D "I'm telling the truth – my brother really did eat my homework."

E "Was it because I burned that book? Or my locker? Or the classroom?"

1

2

3

4

5

Scare-itage ART Show

Use your mad art skills on this page to create a self-portrait monsterpiece for the scare-itage art show. Study your freaky-fab face in a mirror or photograph and sketch the details – then add something extra to turn yourself into a scary-cool monster. Will your artwork be good enough to impress the Board of Deaducation?

SCARY-COOL SEQUENCES

GHOULIA'S working on another puzzle!
Can you help her by drawing the correct
symbol to finish each sequence?

103

TOTALLY *True* OR FREAKISHLY FALSE

Howl much do you know about the student bodies of Monster High? Awaken your brain and decide if these statements are true or false. Circle your answers, then check them on page 175!

1. Skelita Calaveras hails from Scaris, the City of Frights.

TRUE ⬤   **FALSE** ⬤

2. Howleen is Clawdeen Wolf's little sister.

TRUE   **FALSE** ⬤

3. Cleo de Nile's monster pet is a snake called Hissette.

TRUE   **FALSE** ⬤

4. Catty Noir is a famous casketball star.

TRUE   **FALSE**

5. Twyla is the daughter of the Boogey Man.

TRUE ⬤ FALSE ◯

6. Purrsephone and Toralei are twin sisters.

TRUE ⬤ FALSE ◯

7. Gigi Grant loves being stuck in small spaces.

TRUE ◯ FALSE ⬤

8. If you want your portrait sketched, you should ask Catrine de Mew.

TRUE ⬤ FALSE ◯

9. Ghoulia Yelps cannot function without a schedule.

TRUE ◯ FALSE ⬤

10. Draculaura only has fangs for Deuce Gorgon.

TRUE ◯ FALSE ⬤

ANSWERS ON PAGE 175

Dialling DiSaSteR

UGGH NO! Draculaura is freaking out because she accidentally left a terror-ble voicemail for Clawd. Count Fabulous and the other monster pets have decided to help a ghoul out. Can you help them through the maze, to reach Clawd's iCoffin and delete the message?

START

FINISH

ANSWERS ON PAGE 175

NO Ghouls ALLOWED

THE GHOULS AREN'T HAPPY - Deuce, Clawd, Gil and Jackson are having a secret monster boys' night out! Can you spot and circle nine things that have changed in the bottom picture?

107

HORRO-MANCE FOR HOWLEEN

It's the first full moon of the lunar leap year and horro-mance is in the air. Clawdeen warns her little sister, Howleen, to be scareful. But why? Find out by cracking the creeperific code below.

ZOMBIE-DOKU

ANSWERS ON PAGE 175

Ghoulia l-urgh-ves testing her intelligence. Help her by completing this zombie-doku she's working on. Each of the numbers, 1 to 6, should appear once in each column, row and box.

	5			1	
6			2	5	4
		2			5
		6			1
	2		5		
3				4	

ANSWERS ON PAGE 175

SLUMBER PARTY: YETI STYLE!

The ghouls are having a slumber party at **ABBEY'S** house. It's so cold that they need their slippers.

Find the slipper stickers and stick them on the feet of the correct ghoul.

ANSWERS ON PAGE 175

Invasion OF the Ghoul SNATCHERS

After watching a scary movie, Frankie and Draculaura are sure that aliens have invaded Monster High. Help them prove it by unscrambling the names below and working out which are the true student bodies. The others are alien invaders!

1 PTESCRA OTNDVEREGIS

_ _ _ _ _ _ _ _ _ _ _ _ _ _ _ _

2 TTYAC RION

_ _ _ _ _ _ _ _ _

3 ENILA IRVNADE

_ _ _ _ _ _ _ _ _ _ _

4 ENUVS CFMPLTRAY

_ _ _ _ _ _ _ _ _ _ _ _

5 IAFIJREN OLGN

_ _ _ _ _ _ _ _ _ _ _

6 KSELTIA ACVLAERS

_ _ _ _ _ _ _ _ _ _ _ _ _

7 KAFE TTUSDEN

_ _ _ _ _ _ _ _ _ _

8 UDEEC GRNGOO

_ _ _ _ _ _ _ _ _ _

GAME OVER

Help Robecca and Ghoulia wipe *Angry Ghouls* from these monsters' iCoffins!
They want to transmit the virus through the network signal, so work out which
signals lead to the student bodies.

113

Sweet Meow-sic

This is the music room. Some monsters are really musically talented – like Operetta (although she never sings live for fear of making monsters lose their minds) and the purrfect pop star Catty Noir™. She's so creeperifically cool! We can't believe someone so talon-ted is going to our school. Draculaura and I had a blast at her last concert. It was spooktacular!

Use your pens to fill the stage with Frankie and all her GFFs, rocking out to Ms Noir's furbulous werecat beat!

ROCK N' SKUL

HOME ICK HOMEWORK

Here we are in home ick! Ms Kindergrübber gives me pretty good grades – I think she was impressed when I baked a life-sized gingerbread man and brought him to life! Today she wants us to think up recipes that celebrate our ughsome individuality. Mine is a high-voltage energy drink. Wanna try it?

Frankie Stein's joltin' juice

This intensely green smoothie is great at creep-fast time. It tastes super fruity and the energy jolt will really set you up for school!

For two smoothies, you will need:
- 1 banana, cut into slices
- ½ apple or pear, cored and chopped
- 150g seedless white grapes
- 50g fresh spinach leaves, torn
- 200g vanilla yoghurt
- Ice cubes to serve

1. Place all of the ingredients into a blender or food processor.

2. Put the lid on and blend until smooth.

3. Fill tall glasses with ice cubes, then pour the juice over.

4. Leave the smoothies to chill for a couple of minutes and then enjoy.

 Always ask an adult before using sharp knives and blenders. Kitchen kit can be dangerous!

 115

ANSWERS ON PAGE 175

Potion SOLUTIONS

Each of these student bodies wants one of Cleo's ancient potions to help them with something. Can you match up the request with the monster who's written it?

1 GHOULIA IS THE BRAINIEST MONSTER IN THE WHOLE SCHOOL AND SOMETIMES I WORRY THAT I'M NOT SMART ENOUGH FOR HER. I WOULD GIVE MY UNLIFE FOR A POTION TO MAKE ME UBER-INTELLIGENT!

2 Sometimes I just wish monsters would see me as more than a 'little sister'. It would be totally fur-rocious to have a potion that would make them see me as the grown-wolf I know I am.

3 Just once it would be fangtastic to see what I look like. I mean, I'm not vain or anything, but creating a new scare-style when you don't have a reflection is a nightmare!

4 I can't let Toralei steal the lead in the new school play from me! I need to use a potion to make me look boo-tifully young and gore-geous.

Draculaura

SLO MO

Howleen

Cleo de Nile

ANSWERS ON PAGE 175

STEAM'S SCHEDULE

Robecca Steam doesn't have her school timetable saved on her iCoffin … because she doesn't have an iCoffin! She's all about old-school pen and paper. Help her fill out her schedule by finding her subjects in the grid below — look up, down, forwards, backwards and diagonally.

P	H	F	A	R	W	A	H	Z	B	N	M	Q	P	B	A	O	I	L
M	H	Z	X	P	L	I	K	F	G	A	S	D	H	I	L	N	B	D
W	A	Y	M	Z	P	O	L	D	A	C	L	A	W	T	R	F	G	R
R	S	E	S	E	G	A	U	G	N	A	L	D	A	E	D	Q	D	A
V	S	M	N	I	Z	X	C	D	I	U	E	F	S	O	D	A	T	G
R	T	R	D	A	C	A	E	Q	W	N	O	L	A	L	D	E	A	O
V	U	N	B	Z	L	A	S	S	G	E	O	G	S	O	Y	T	Y	N
A	D	P	H	R	A	S	L	E	W	W	Z	M	A	G	E	C	H	O
J	Y	L	M	N	W	V	S	D	B	Z	D	E	T	Y	R	T	S	M
N	H	B	R	X	C	K	H	G	E	O	G	R	E	P	H	Y	A	E
N	O	M	R	S	U	Z	D	D	V	A	I	R	Y	E	W	F	W	T
A	W	A	L	H	L	D	J	U	T	R	D	S	H	C	S	X	Z	R
Y	L	T	I	A	O	Q	A	D	Z	G	H	U	L	K	C	Z	B	Y
E	A	M	A	D	U	S	E	C	P	D	Z	E	C	A	S	P	O	Y
N	D	S	E	Z	S	K	S	L	P	S	W	I	C	A	E	A	P	K
J	H	S	A	Q	I	Y	E	D	S	V	E	B	V	S	T	F	G	H
B	E	C	N	E	I	C	S	D	A	M	M	S	D	X	M	I	I	O
O	P	R	E	D	X	S	A	Q	O	Z	I	O	V	B	M	N	O	R
P	L	J	G	I	T	E	A	H	D	X	S	Y	F	H	I	K	N	N

BITEOLOGY
DEAD LANGUAGES
GE-OGRE-PHY

DRAGONOMETRY
STUDY HOWL
MAD SCIENCE

PHYSICAL DEAD-UCATION
CLAWCULOUS
HOME ICK

ANSWERS ON PAGE 175

MONSTER PETS

Here are more Monster High student bodies with their beast friends. Find the stickers that match the monster pet silhouettes!

RHUEN

My phantom furittus (that's 'ferret' to you!).

CAPTAIN PENNY

Every penguin needs a rocket pack to fly.

SHIVER

A woolly mammoth with a tough hide.

118

ROUX

Griffins make the best beasties!

CHEWLIAN

He's got a snappy personality.

PERSEUS

Two tails and loads of rat-i-chewed!

119

MEM-URRGH-Y TEST

It's time to test your monster memory! Look at this scary-cool snap, then cover it up and try to answer the questions on the opposite page.

ANSWERS ON PAGE 175

MEM-URRGH-Y TEST

1 Which ghoul has a tail? ....

2 What does Frankie have on her head? ....

3 Clawdeen's earring is which famous landmark? ....

4 Which two ghouls have their hair up? ....

5 Is Jinafire standing on the far left? ....

6 Who is standing between Clawdeen and Frankie? ....

7 Who is standing between Frankie and Jinafire? ....

YOUR StUDENt Profile

You know all about the student bodies at Monster High, but they want to know all about you! Create your own student profile on this page.

NAME:

AGE:

FREAKY FLAW:

FAVOURITE FOOD:

FAVOURITE COLOUR:

FAVOURITE ACTIVITY:

KILLER STYLE:

PET:

PET PEEVE:

122

CREATE a Monster

If you could put together a scary-cool new Monster High student, who would they be and what would they look like? Let your imagination run wild and sketch their hair, make-up and killer style below.

Freaky February

Freaky February is a special time at Monster High. It's the month deadicated to appreciating one another' freaky flaws in all their glory. It's a scary-cool celebration of uniqueness! Freaky February is especially important for vampire and werewolf students – it's the one time they put aside their age-old feud and appreciate each other's qualities.

Make a list of the things that make Draculaura a total one-off. Describe all her most fangtastic attributes, then turn your attention to Clawdeen. What makes the talon-ted werewolf so ugh-mazing? When you've finished, draw a picture of the drop-dead gorgeous duo in action.

Draculaura is freaky-fangtastic because...........................
....
....
....
....

Clawdeen is freaky-furbulous because...........................
....
....
....

Minute Mind Mash

Draculaura is totally over-excited – it's her birthday this month! The ghouls are making sure that she gets trick or treated with a party and a putrid pastry of a cake. Give yourself 60 seconds to look at this photo, then cover it up with a sheet of paper. Now take your chances answering the questions below.

Who is in the photo with Draculaura?

....

What is he wearing on his head?

....

What type of footwear is he wearing?

....

4. Is the mystery boy standing on the left or the right of Draculaura?

....

5. What is he about to give the birthday girl?

....

6. How many tiers does Draculaura's cake have?

....

7. Does it have candles?

....

8. How many earrings did you spot in the photo?

....

ANSWERS ON PAGE 175

Lost in Scaris

Scaris is an amazing place, but its dank alleys have so many twists, turns and dead-ends, it's easy to get lost. The Monster High ghouls are on a night out with their guide Rochelle, but she has got separated from the group. Can you help the GFFs pick their way back through the spooky streets?

START

FINISH

HOWL MONITOR'S WARNING WORDSEARCH

Rochelle's been given the job of Howl Monitor! It's up to her to ensure that the students don't loiter, litter or lay about when they should all be in class. She has issued warnings to the 10 students listed below. Can you find their names in the grid? The letters you seek could be running in any direction!

N	H	Y	D	O	L	W	O	E	M	T	S	X
N	E	O	P	U	R	R	S	E	M	O	P	H
I	P	C	L	A	D	W	O	L	S	F	O	E
E	I	F	E	T	O	R	A	L	E	O	L	A
T	R	R	C	R	H	Y	D	A	D	O	C	T
S	T	A	L	S	O	Y	Q	U	S	D	N	H
E	S	S	A	T	T	O	D	S	L	U	O	B
I	I	I	W	E	I	E	N	E	O	D	M	U
K	E	M	D	U	V	E	I	H	M	O	I	R
N	L	O	W	O	N	G	Y	M	O	A	S	N
A	A	C	O	J	N	R	O	M	I	L	A	S
R	R	D	L	M	A	N	N	Y	T	A	U	R
F	O	A	F	R	A	K	I	E	R	R	S	H
O	T	S	U	L	U	M	O	R	H	O	K	T

MANNY TAUR
CLAWD WOLF
FRANKIE STEIN

HEATH BURNS
HOLT HYDE
HOODUDE VOODOO
SLO MO

ROMULUS
SIMON CLOPS
TORALEI STRIPE

A mischievous kitty is about to be added to Rochelle's list. Can you locate her name in the grid? Now write it below.

....

Mad Science Fair

Mad science at Monster High is anything but dull. Lessons have seen students shrinking themselves to the size of flies and the teacher, Mr Hackington, being attacked by just-hatched baby gargoyles during an egg-rearing project!

Mr Hack has set a challenging new homework this month. Each pupil has to create an invention for the annual Monster High Mad Science Fair. Fancy putting in an entry? Previous stars of the show have included science queen Ghoulia's electro-magnetic pulse mega-machine and a cool gizmo that turns rubbish into clean, green fuel.

Check out the zombie's projects, then create your own weird and wacky invention. Mr Hack is counting on you to land that prize!

As
Arsenic

T
Titanium

Fr
rancium

En
Scary

Ds
Darmstadtium

Sc
Scandium

H
Helium

I
Iodine

G
Gho

U
Uranium

Ni
Nickel

C
Carbon

Be
Beryllium

A
Arse

F
Franc

F
Fluorine

Re
Rhenium

A
Go

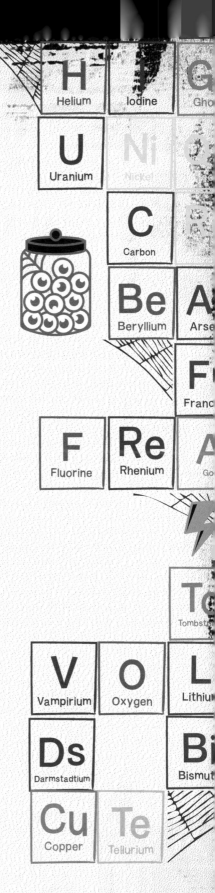

To
Tombst

V
Vampirium

O
Oxygen

L
Lithiu

Ds
Darmstadtium

Bi
Bismut

Cu
Copper

Te
Tellurium

It's Homecarnage!

The annual Homecarnage Dance is just weeks away and the whole of Monster High is ringing with the screams, howls, moans and roars of excited students. Cleo de Nile has organized a committee to run the event, but they're having trouble agreeing on a theme. Draw lines to match each ghoul to her Homecarnage theme idea, then check your answers.

ENCHANTMENT UNDER THE SEA

CAN'T FIGHT THE MOONLIGHT

A VAMPIRE'S KISS IS JUST A KISS

GREEN SCREAM

GRAVEYARD GLITZ

CATACOMB CHAOS

MIDNIGHT IN SCARIS

TIME OF MY UNLIFE

EGYPTIAN ALLURE

WINTER WONDERLAND

Clawdeen Wolf™

Rochelle Goyle™

Lagoona Blue™

Cleo de Nile™

Draculaura™

Frankie Stein™

Venus McFlytrap™

Abbey Bominable™

Robecca Steam™

Spectra Vondergeist™

130

MONSTER HIGH™

School Sculpture

New ghoul in school Rochelle Goyle really wants to make a big impression at Monster High. She's even volunteered to carve a sculpture of Headmistress Bloodgood™ for the Homecarnage Dance! Can you help her finish the job? Draw in the Head's head.

Ghoulia Yelps™

ANSWERS ON PAGE 175

OK, so she's not the most communicative of students, but then show us a zombie who is! Behind those horn-rimmed glasses is a smart brain with an awesome appetite for learning. Can you ace her history homework? If you're having a nightmare, the answers are on page 175.

Ghoulia's History Homework

1.
Fill in the blanks below to complete an alternative name for the Abominable Snowman.
Y _ _ _

2.
Ancient vampire Dracula is said to come from...
a. Argentina
b. The United States
c. Transylvania

3.
In Ancient Egypt rulers were often buried in tombs within which triangular structures?

....

4.
Which metal is most dangerous to a werewolf?
a. Silver
b. Gold
c. Platinum

5.
In Greek mythology, the Goddess Athena punished Medusa by turning her to stone.
True
False

6.
A distant cousin to the Sea Monster, the Loch Ness Monster, is said to lurk in which European country?

....

YOU CAN'T HURRY GENIUS!

133

UPLOADING PIC.....

It's the Homecarnage Dance and **SPECTRA** has uploaded a pic to her blog. But someone messed with the picture before it was published!

HERE'S THE ORIGINAL PHOTO ...

1 2 3 4 5

... AND HERE'S
WHAT WAS POSTED!

Can you spot 10 things that have been changed? Add a sticker below for each difference you spot.

6 7 8 9 10

GPA QUIZ
(Ghastly Point Average)

At Monster High we're expected to achieve eek-cellence – we get tested every term! How much do you know about the monster world? Check your ghastly point average with this fiendishly difficult Scary Aptitude Test.

Are you as scarily smart as Ghoulia Yelps? It's time to put your monstrous mind to the test. Grab a pen and get scribbling!

1. The practice of chanting and performing freaky dance moves to support a team is called ...

A. sport-spooking ☐
B. fearleading ☐
C. rollermazing ☐

2. Name a sport played with a ball and a net, commonly practised by monsters at Monster High.

....

3. Unscramble the letters to reveal Ms Kindergrübber's ghastly subject.

O H E M   K I C

....

4. Which of these could cause problems for members of the Monster High swimming team?

A. Having Frankie Stein on the team ☐
B. A creature lurking in the deep end ☐
C. Rochelle Goyle diving in the pool ☐

5. At the annual Mad Science Fair, student bodies exhibit work that they've invented during which teacher's class?

....

6. Which teacher at Monster High famously does not give As?

....

7. What are the series of dark caves and caverns beneath the school known as?

....

8. When not in class, where should student bodies store their possessions?

....

9. Pets are not allowed in the classrooms.

True ☐
False ☐

10. Who at Monster High beat both Mr Rotter and Mr Hackington to scoop the coveted Creature of the Year Award?

....

11. Which two dates in the diary add up to the worst bad-luck day ever?

A. Friday the 13th and Valentine's Day ☐
B. Halloween and Day of the Dead ☐
C. Friday the 13th and October 31st ☐

12. Failing a test or getting a very low grade can mean your parents are called in for a ...

A. Parent-Creature Conference ☐
B. Reaper's Report ☐
C. Bloodgood bashing ☐

13. Which of these is NOT an extra-scare-icular activity at Monster High?

A. Fashion Entrepreneurs' Club ☐
B. Comic Book Club ☐
C. Scream Team ☐

So ... how do you measure up?

× × × × × × × × × ××× × ××

0-5
Drear oh drear! You're not eek-xactly high voltage. This monster must try harder.

6-10
You've done some of your haunting homework, but you'll need to swot up on a few more freaky facts before you come top of the class.

11-13
Ugh-mazing! With that Ghastly Point Average, you could even give Ghoulia the shivers!

DEAD POETS' SOCIETY

A. Ode to .... **B.**

With a skull for a face,
Some would say he's a freak.
But he gives good advice,
If you've had a bad week.
You can go seek him out,
He's a really kind creature.
He's the Monster High counsellor,
Not really a teacher.

The Chosen One

Oh Princess of dreams,
Oh Princess of dreams,
Your scarabs and icons,
Are the stuff of screams.
Oh ghoul of such beauty,
So gilded and gold,
Five thousand years plus,
Still you never grow old.

C. ....'s

Haunting Beauty

Wooooooooooooooo!
Hooooooooooooooo!
Other worldy ghoul,
Floating and haunting,
The halls of this school.
Glamour and gossip,
Trail in your wake.
Wooooooooooooooo!
Hooooooooooooooo!
A great ghoulfriend,
For some monster you'll make.

D. All About

Frankie made me,
When she needed some dates.
But it didn't work out,
So now we're just mates.
But on this ughsome ghoul,
I still have a big crush.
She's a high-voltage babe,
And I think she's just lush!

Clever lyricist Operetta is penning a special song for Homecarnage. Holt Hyde™ will have to play the tune on his decks because no one can listen to Operetta's voice live without going crazy! She's been writing a few rhymes about the guys in school. Can you work out which students and teachers are the subjects of her songs?

E.

Don't Mess With

....

Armed with a rolling pin,
On her head is a scarf.
Her cute smile makes you think
That she's up for a laugh.
But do not be fooled,
For she's strict as can be,
And that rolling pin's spiked,
Mess around and you'll see!

F. Look Out for

....

Half-shaved hair,
And skin so green.
A bolder ghoul,
You've never seen.
But if some monster,
With her entwines.
He could get tangled,
In those vines.

139

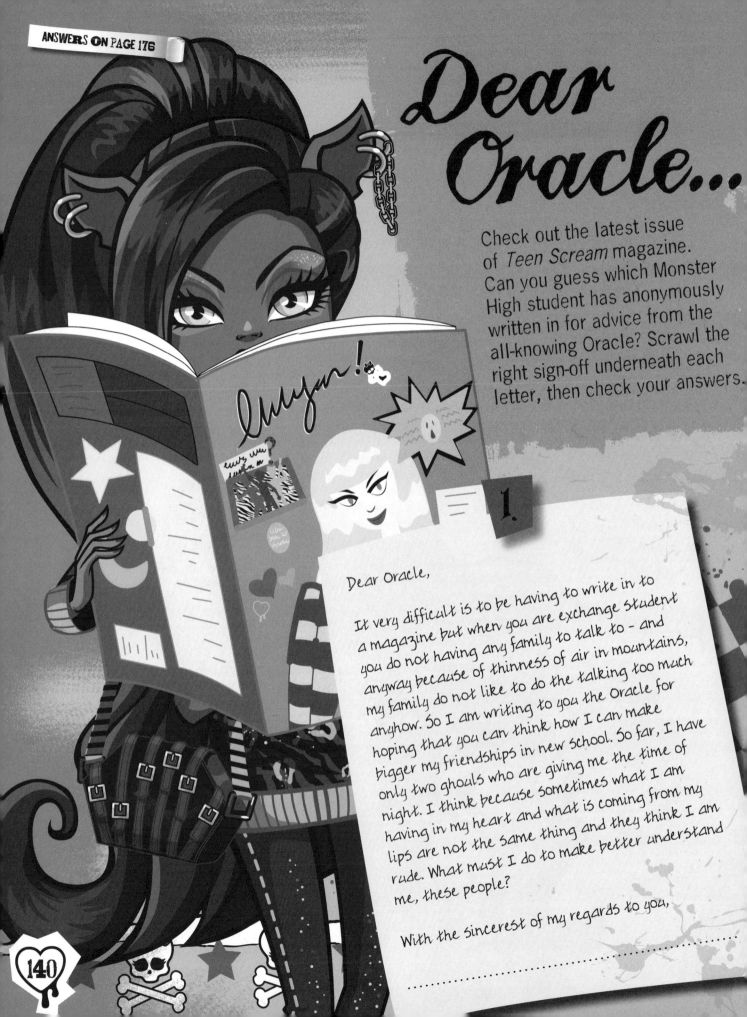

Dear Oracle...

Check out the latest issue of *Teen Scream* magazine. Can you guess which Monster High student has anonymously written in for advice from the all-knowing Oracle? Scrawl the right sign-off underneath each letter, then check your answers.

1.

Dear Oracle,

It very difficult is to be having to write in to a magazine but when you are exchange student you do not having any family to talk to – and anyway because of thinness of air in mountains, my family do not like to do the talking too much anyhow. So I am writing to you the Oracle for hoping that you can think how I can make bigger my friendships in new school. So far, I have only two ghouls who are giving me the time of night. I think because sometimes what I am having in my heart and what is coming from my lips are not the same thing and they think I am rude. What must I do to make better understand me, these people?

With the sincerest of my regards to you,

2.

Dear Oracle,

Can you die from love if you are already undead? I think I might be in danger of this happening to me! There is a totes ughsome guy at school who almost restarts my heart every time I see him. We are kind of dating, but I am friends with one of his family members and it's a little awkward at times. Should I cool it so my GFF feels happier, even though being without him feels like being stuck outside on a sunny day?

Yours achingly,

3.

Dear Oracle,

I totally hope that you can help me because I am like on the verge of doing something revoltage! There's this certain someone who is totally ruining my life. The ghoul in question does everything in her power to make me feel small and to mess things up for me. I just discovered that she's been keeping a major secret from my dad who (falsely) thinks she's the asp's elbow! Should I blow her cover and tell him she's lost her job?

Laters,

4.

Dear Oracle,

ME and another guy are trapped in the most bizarre love triangle EVER! WE both like the same ghoul. I hardly EVER SEE him around school — I think hE must skip class a lot (how lamE?) and I don't likE thE sound of him at all. But I'VE bEEn having thESE blackouts and thE othEr day, thE ghoul of my nightmarES brings mE round and tElls mE that mE and this othEr guy — wE'rE likE thE samE pErson. I don't know what to think, it sounds crazy, but shE's a prEtty switchEd on, high-voltagE ghoul. AftEr this, shE gavE mE thE cold shouldEr. What's my nExt movE?

From,

ANSWERS ON PAGE 176

heads Will Roll!

Students! I am less than impressed. You all know perfectly well that the catacombs are out of bounds while we attempt to catch and vaccinate the Monster High dragon. Unless you have a valid reason for being down there, you are going to be spending the rest of the year in dead-tention!

Match each student with the excuse they are most likely to have given.

1

2

3

4

5

A
"I was indulging in some research ahead of Mr Hackington's Creature Spotting Field Trip next week. Preparation is key to attainment!"

B
"I was doing the skultimate roller-mazing. When I can't get to mountains for snowboard, is next best thing."

C
"Awwww! Are you kidding? I'm already in dead-tention! Mr Rotter sent me down here to clean the Pit of Horror again!"

D
"Li'l ol' me? I was on my way to the soundproof recording studio darlin' – it's the only place I can sing without anyone getting hurt."

E
"I'm sorry! I was wrong to disobey yo but I just wanted t see my dad's old laboratory again. I love that he went Monster High too!"

BOO'S HOO IN THE 'COMBS?

ANSWERS ON PAGE 176

tudy the shadows, then write the correct
ame underneath each fiend. Don't freak
you get stuck – the names are printed at
ne bottom of the page to help you.

I spend a lot of time in
the catacombs. Firstly,
I'm always looking out
for my dad, who was last
seen in these dark caverns.
Secondly, it's a great
place to practise stunts
in my rocket boots.
The catacombs are busy
today and some prankster
has snuffed out the flaming
torches. Can you help me
work out who's who?

1

2

3

5

6

7

4

8

ABBEY
BOMINABLE

CLAWD
WOLF

JINAFIRE LONG

TORALEI STRIPE

OODUDE
VOODOO

VENUS
MCFLYTRAP

DRACULAURA

SKELITA CALAVERAS

143

Fierce Fashion Show

The Fierce Fashion Show is the highlight of the extra-scare-icular calendar for anyone who's anyone in school! Monster High's Fashion Entrepreneurs' Club always attend in full force. Clawdeen Wolf, the school's fiercest fashionista, never misses a meeting.

Clawdeen can't wait to get started on her designs for the show. All she needs now is some monstrous inspiration! Can you help her put together a mood board for an ugh-mazing new collection? Use the opposite page to stick in, scribble and sketch all of your ideas. What would you like to see the Monster High ghouls wearing next year? Tape in scraps of fabric or wrapping paper, cut freaky fabulous photos out of magazines and sketch spooky ideas to create a dead cool theme. Get styling!

ANSWERS ON PAGE 176

Great Balls of Fire

Holt Hyde sets the decks on fire with his scary-cool mixes! Operetta's helping the hottie compile his playlist for next month's Dance of the Dead Disco. Wanna see it? Unscramble the anagrams below to reveal each track. If you get stuck, use the list on the facing page to help you unravel each song title. And look at the artists' names for a clue! When you've cracked each track name, write it on the playlist.

1. RIEEE NEAMIE BY **JUSTIN BITER**

2. TIEB EM BEYAM BY **SCARY RAH JEEPERS**

3. GELSIN MOBSIZE (TUP A IRNG NO TI) BY **BEETLEBOUNCÉ**

4. LOUGH RIGL LETSY BY **PSYCHOTIC**

5. SNAZZIERTOM BY **LADY GHOULA**

6. EW EAR VEERN REVE GANGFIN TOU THREEGOT BY **TERROR SWIFT**

7. TUJS HET YAW EW WHOL BY THE **JAUNDICE BROTHERS**

8. EH LFWO BY **SHRIEKEER**

9. RICHELL BY **FRIGHTFUL JACKSON**

10. HET FAMEROSE MOTHANP OF ETH AROPE (MERIX) BY **CRESCENDA VON HAMMERSTON**

Dance of the Dead Playlist

1: ....

2: ....

3: ....

4: ....

5: ....

6: ....

7: ....

8: ....

9: ....

10: ....

- Ghoul Girl Style
- Monsterazzi
- He Wolf
- Chiller
- Bite Me Maybe
- We Are Never Ever Fanging Out Together
- Single Zombies (Put a Ring On It)
- Eerie Meanie
- Just the Way We Howl
- The Fearsome Phantom of the Opera Theme (Remix)

Bonus track!

Can you think up a bonus track for Operetta to add to the playlist?

....

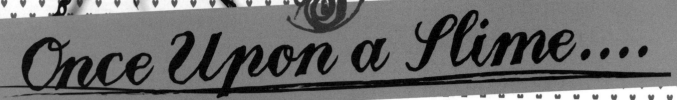

Once Upon a Slime....

Lou Zarr loves to set homework – it helps him forget that he's a mere substitute creature at Monster High. Ula D can't wait to get started on his latest assignment! The students have been asked to imagine a scary story. How will yours begin?

Creepy Characters

Who will star in your terrifying tale? Will you draw from your ghoulfriends a frenemies at Monster High, feature one o the beasties below or invent a brand-new monster of your own?

* Scarlett the Skeleton's daughter
* Nestor and Vanda the Loch Ness Monster's twin children
* Esme the Seawitch's daughter
* Orlando, nephew of the Ogre

Woeful Words

Use a smattering of these adjectives to add an awful atmosphere to your story:

* Hideous
* Horrific
* Terrible
* Gruesome
* Shocking
* Scary
* Creepy
* Hair-raising
* Eerie
* Spinechilling

Spooky Spots

Will the story unfold at Monster High, or in one of these grim locations?

* The Coffin Bean (coffee shop)
* The Maul
* Gloom Beach
* Skull Shores
* The Bleak Bowl (bowling alley)
* Smogsnorts Vampyr Academy

Ghoulish Goings On

The first line is always the toughest. You could start with one of these:

* Aaaaargh! A curdling cry rolled across the sand at Gloom Beach....
* It was just another day among the undead....
* The lights went up and a thousand howls filled the air as Justin Biter walked on stage....

Once upon a slime....

Ghoulia's Ghastly Word Grid

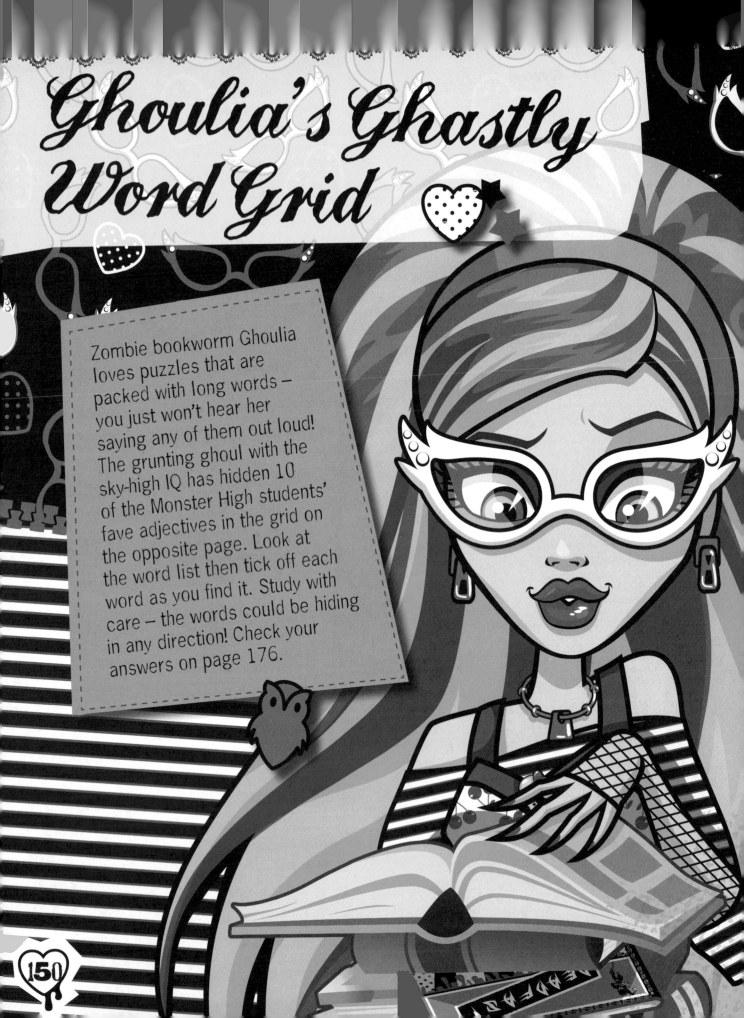

Zombie bookworm Ghoulia loves puzzles that are packed with long words — you just won't hear her saying any of them out loud! The grunting ghoul with the sky-high IQ has hidden 10 of the Monster High students' fave adjectives in the grid on the opposite page. Look at the word list then tick off each word as you find it. Study with care — the words could be hiding in any direction! Check your answers on page 176.

```
C A N Z F A U G H M A Z I N G E
R C L A W S O M E A Y B N C E N
E T J Y A O G O Q U G J G I H I
E F R B H U H S F Y O T R F H H
P Y O A I H S U G Z M A A I H F
A C J F L B O O X F L X I R R S
F I S J S U M I N U T E N E N E
I T F D R J C G C H G A J P N O
E S N B E A G A H A J O I E O L
R A H A E J T T T P P H D E L A
C T Q U N K M L N K N L M R N G
E G F A A G V O G X O E R C N G
Q N X E R N D V A G H O D A G G
U A R P O K C A T K O O P S G A
P F A N G L O O C Y R A C S A
```

CLAWSOME   GOLDEN
CREEPERIFIC   SCARY-COOL
FANGTASTIC   SPOOKTACULAR
FIERCE   UGH-MAZING
FREAKTACULAR   VOLTAGIOUS

ANSWERS ON PAGE 176

TRUE OR FALSE

Are you Monster High's biggest fan?
Test your knowledge with this creeperific quiz!
Stick a 'true' or 'false' sticker next to each
statement, then check your answers.

1 Frankie sometimes falls apart – literally.

True

2 Cleo's sister is called Nefertiti.

False

3 Operetta is Rochelle Goyle's pet.

False

4 The lockers at Monster High are coffin-shaped.

True

5 Cleo is the captain of the Fear Squad.

True

6 Draculaura can turn into a bat whenever she wants to.

False

7 Deuce can turn people to stone.

True

8 Toralei Stripe is best friends with Clawdeen.

False

9 Sloman "Slo Mo" Mortavitch is a zombie.

True

10 Bloodgood is Monster High's headless headmistress.

True

ANSWERS ON PAGE 176

HANDBAG
MiX-up

The ghouls' handbags are all mixed up! Draw lines to match each ghoul with her own bag (the one that matches her unique scary-cool style).

Grim Grid

Mr Rotter, the dead languages teacher, loves grim grids – the monster version of the crossword. He's always asking students to complete them! Try your hand at this one. Make sure you finish before he lumbers around to check on your progress....

Clues

Across

1. Surname of the Monster High drama teacher. (5)
2. Pointed teeth seen on vampires and werewolves. (5)
3. _____ of the Opera, father of Operetta. (7)
4. Headmistress Bloodgood's pet. (9)
5. Carnivorous fish often found in the Monster High swimming pool. (7)
6. Physical _____. An active lesson on the Monster High slimetable. (11)
7. Box used for burial and as a locker at Monster High. (6)
8. Surname of the school's home ick teacher. (13)
9. Metallic colour and phrase Cleo uses to describe something awesome. (6)
10. Hard material that victims of Deuce Gorgon's stare find themselves transformed into. (5)
11. Name of a popular monster magazine. (4,6)
12. "It's _____!" Exclamation Frankie's father shouts each morning when seeing his daughter. (5)
13. Clawdeen's favourite food. (5)

Down

1. Name of Frankie's pet puppy. (6)
2. Type of monster, parent of Abbey Bominable. (4)
3. Checked pattern often used on cloth and frequently worn by Frankie. (5)
4. Bright colour favoured by Draculaura. (4)
5. First name of Miss Vondergeist, a ghostly student at Monster High. (7)
6. Cloth wrappings used in ancient Egypt on bodies and often seen trailing from Cleo de Nile. (8)
7. Monster High activity involving dancing in a group and performing cheers. (11)
8. Monster High version of 'Homecoming'. (11)
9. Cleo's older sister. (6)
10. Hall where Monster High students eat lunch. (11)
11. Skin-hydrating product used in large amounts by Lagoona Blue. (11)
12. Word meaning 'girlfriend' in the monster world. (11)
13. Team sport like basketball, played at Monster High. (10)
14. Species of animal owned as a pet by Jackson Jekyll and Holt Hyde. (9)
15. Website where monsters post video clips. (10)
16. Warm material often worn by Abbey Bominable. (3)
17. Name of Cleo's scaly pet. (8)
18. 'The _____'. Advice column in teen monster magazine. (6)
19. Slow, uncommunicative type of monster found at Monster High. (6)
20. Cleo is afraid of this…. (4)

Fancy Fearleading?

Want to give Cleo de Nile and the gang a run for their money at the Monster Mashionals? Round up your most creeperific ghoulfriends and set up a fearsome new fearleading squad!

SCARY STYLE

Fearleaders need to look the part! Raid your wardrobe for killer pieces that will allow you to move while looking dead cool. Don't worry if you can't lay your paws on a set of fearleading uniforms – being a monster is all about embracing your uniqueness. Simply pick a theme colour for the squad, then add your own twist with accessories that are totally 'you'.

MONSTER MAKE-UP

For that extra Monster High touch use face paints to add fangs, a ghoulish pallor or a Draculaura-inspired heart-shaped beauty mark.

PAWFECT POM POMS

No fearleading squad is complete without pom poms! The Monster High ghouls shake black, pink or a combination of the two, but you can pick any shade to complement your fiercely fabulous look.

MAD MOVES

These mad moves are so this century, they are guaranteed to send shivers up the spines of any rival! Work some of these into your fearleading routines.

Cleo's Kick

This move is Cleo's trademark. Stand side by side and place one arm on your GFF's shoulder. Kick the opposite leg high in the air. If you're really flexible you could try kicking to the side and holding your leg up near your ear, by the ankle. Other squad members add drama by kneeling, putting their palms together above their head and moving their head side to side like an Egyptian.

Roarsome Roll

Kneel in a row, then do synchronized forward and backward rolls. When you find your feet, jump up and howl at the Moon!

Clawdeen's Claws

Make claws with your hands then 'pounce' on imaginary prey.

Stein's Stalk and Shimmy

Stalk to the left and then to the right for four paces. Next shimmy your shoulders back and forth, while shaking your pom poms.

The Ghoulia Lurch

Put your arms forward like a zombie and lurch forwards for four steps and back for four. Now move to the right for four and to the left for four.

Terrifying Tunes

Fearleading routines need truly creeperific backing music! Why not set your routine to We Are Monster High?

We are monsters, we are proud.
We are monsters, say it loud.

High school's a horror, can't get out of my bed.
Everybody's talking, but it's not in my head.
They say don't be different, be like them instead,
But they can't keep us down,
'Cause we're Monster High bred!

The clock is striking 13 (Whoa oh oh oh)
It's time to cheer for your team (Whoa oh oh oh)
You're the ghoulest ghoul by far,
So don't be afraid of who you are.

'Cause tonight we're gonna leave our fears behind.
We're in it together.
Stepping out and we're letting our spirits fly,
Stay fierce forever.

Wa wa wa wa oh – freak out if you dare.
Wa wa wa wa oh – your best nightmare.
Don't stop rocking your right to fright,
We are Monster High!

We are monsters, we are proud.
We are monsters, say it loud.

Perfectly imperfect and we do it our way.
United, not divided, won't get cast away.
They say go run and hide, but I just gotta say:
We're drop-dead gorgeous each and every day.

The clock is striking 13 (Whoa oh oh oh)
It's time to scream for your team (Whoa oh oh oh)
We don't have to say goodbye,
'Cause friends like these will never die.

'Cause tonight we're gonna leave our fears behind.
We're in it together.
Come on! It's time to let our spirits fly,
Stay fierce forever.

Wa wa wa wa oh – freak out if you dare.
Wa wa wa wa oh – your best nightmare.
Don't stop rocking your right to fright,
We are Monster High!

We are monsters, we are proud.
We are monsters, say it loud.
We are Monster High!

ANSWERS ON PAGE 176

Bell-Tower Beauties

Rochelle and I can both be found floating around the bell tower. I monster-watch from up here, looking for inspiration for my column. Rochelle just feels most at home when she's near (or on) the roof.

How well do you know Monster High's bell-tower beauties? Underline the words that sum up Rochelle in grey and those that make you think of Spectra in purple.

Rock Candy   Violet   Protective

Griffin   Silk   Angel Cake   Pale

Rhuen   Persistent   Transparent

Floating   Disgruntled   Chains

Roux   Scaris   Kind   Haunting

Defensive   Ferret   Curious

Iron   Stained Glass   Journalism

Architecture   Pigeons   Sculpting

Rattle   Ghostly Gossip   Grey

158

Spectra and Rochelle have a ghoul's-eye view of comings and groanings at Monster High. What do you think they've just spotted? Draw the scene here!

ANSWERS ON PAGE 176

READ aLL aBOuT iT!

MONSTER HIGH

Monster Mashionals

MONSTER HIGH SMASHES THE MASHIONALS!

B-TEAM HAS THE X-FACTOR

The B-team of Monster High pulled off a freaktacular victory at the Monster Mashionals yesterday, beating the A-team with a perfectly co-ordinated display of fearleading.

It was a tense finale with the B-team of captain Cleo de Nile, Frankie Stein, Clawdeen Wolf, Draculaura and Ghoulia Yelps going up against big sister Nefera de Nile's team of Toralei Stripe and twins Purrsephone and Meowlody.

Clutching the trophy, Cleo said, "We trained so hard for this, whenever and wherever we were allowed to train. They made it really hard for us, but we did it!" She went on, "It was our destiny to win. I'm so proud of my boos. They are fierce!"

> "IT WAS **OUR DESTINY TO WIN.** I'M SO PROUD OF MY BOOS. THEY ARE FIERCE!"

The A-team losers

The B-team winner

SPECTRA is putting together pages for the school newspaper about the Monster Mashionals. Can you help her by sticking in pictures to go with her captions?

PROUD BLOODGOOD PRAISES GHOULS

"Another school victory! Here at Monster High we take our extra-scare-icular activities very seriously, and I'm delighted that the ghouls brought home the trophy from Mashionals. They are a credit to the school."

Headmistress Bloodgood.

IN OTHER NEWS....

NEFERA IN TROUBLE WITH DAD

Nefera de Nile in BIG trouble.

Thunder and lightning shook the de Nile pyramid yesterday when The Mummy returned home from his trip. Sparks flew when he found out that his daughter, Nefera, had stolen all his charms and amulets. I think it is fair to say that Nefera might not be seen out for a very long time....

SOMETHING TO HOWL ABOUT

The Fear Squad put their trophy next to the Spirit Staff they won at Gloom Beach. Cleo said, "Our coach, Scary Murphy, really believed in us. We can't thank her enough. We'd like to thank our freaktastic friends, too, who were there for us all the way."

"OUR COACH, SCARY MURPHY, REALLY BELIEVED IN US."

Cleo de Nile with the trophy!

ANSWERS ON PAGE 176

GHOUL RULES

ROCHELLE is the head of the safety team at Monster High and she knows that two of these school rules are wrong. Do you know which ones? Put a cross next to them. Now check your answers. If you were right, give yourself a gold Safety Badge sticker!

1 All monsters must eat meat at lunchtimes in the creepateria.

2 No heads, hands or feet should be separated from bodies during school hours.

3 Students should venture only into the known areas of the catacombs – no further!

4 All zombies should start heading to class half an hour early. Slowness is no excuse for lateness!

5 Always look Deuce Gorgon in the eyes when his sunglasses are off.

DESIGN a LOGO

After their success at Monster Mashionals, the **FEAR SQUAD** is getting a new look. Design them a logo and add it to their flag. Go ghouls, go!

Monster
high rules

Here we have the school pool. I'm not in here that much — electricity and water are not a good mix! I was forced to take a dip on the day I dropped Draculaura's fave necklace into the water by mistake. I had to swim down to get it back from the huge creature that lurks in the pool's dark caverns.

Lagoona's a monster you'd totally catch in the pool! She's aquatically ugh-mazing! Use your fave pens or pencils to add some fin-tastic new designs to her swimwear.

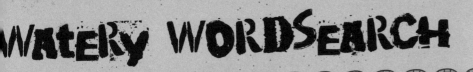

WATERY WORDSEARCH

Dip a webbed toe into the watery world of Lagoona Blue. Her scare-itage as the 'salty' daughter of the Sea Monster means there's nobody faster or fiercer to captain the Monster High Swim Team to championship victory. The grid below contains 12 words that are always on the tip of Lagoona's tongue. Tick them off the list as you find them. Remember, they could be lurking in any direction – horizontally, vertically or diagonally!

S	M	I	W	S	I	M	I	N	G	U	O
A	N	T	E	N	I	R	O	L	H	C	L
L	P	R	E	T	A	W	H	S	E	R	F
T	T	O	T	V	A	N	O	A	P	J	S
W	U	S	U	S	E	A	N	S	R	F	W
A	W	E	L	N	B	O	H	S	I	F	F
T	C	V	E	L	G	E	T	U	N	E	I
E	L	A	V	R	I	T	I	S	D	R	N
R	O	W	A	G	O	G	D	I	U	A	S
S	R	P	S	E	V	W	E	T	E	R	E
R	H	S	N	E	P	T	U	N	E	G	F
Y	S	A	E	D	M	J	V	T	N	G	I

Final Stroke!

Can you find the extra, 13th word hiding in the grid? It's the chemical that makes Lagoona's scales dry out – and the reason she has to slap on tombs of monsturizer!

- - - - - - - -

SEA   **NEPTUNE**   **GILLS**

OCEANOGRAPHY   **SWIM**   **FINS**

WAVES   **FISH**   **TIDE**

SALTWATER   **FRESHWATER**   **SURF**

165

Venus Mc-Facepaints

Venus McFlytrap has made a lot of new friends since she enrolled at Monster High. Abbey loves her straightforward attitude and Frankie's even helped her organize a fashion show! Draculaura is totally wowed by Venus' new take on make-up – freaky facepainting.

Can you help the fashionista create some snappy facepaint designs for her friends? Doodle your design first and then fill it in, choosing a scary-cool colour scheme to suit each ghoul's style.

167

Date Dilemma

Abbey hasn't yet found a date for the Dance of the Dead. Now she's starting to freak out! Her GFFs have set up a speed-dating (or 'hurry-up-dating' as Abbey calls it) event to help her bag a monster for the evening. Read what each one has to say for himself, then draw lines to match the notes to the names at the bottom of the page.

A

WELL HELLO GHOULFRIEND, YOU'RE LOOKING PRETTY HOT FOR ONE SO COLD! HOW'D YOU LIKE ME TO TAKE YOU TO THE DANCE OF THE DEAD? YOU'D BE HEAD AND SHOULDERS ABOVE THE DANCE FLOOR CROWD SO AT LEAST I'D GET TO SEE YOU FROM MY DJ BOOTH. I'VE BEEN SINGLE SINCE SPLITTING FROM HOTTIE FRANKIE STEIN. STICK WITH ME AND WE'LL SET THE SCHOOL ON FIRE!

B

I just came along with a friend, to see what's what really, I've got casketball practice in a minute, so I gotta go and anyway, I'm kinda dating this cute pink-wearing vampire.

C

A DATE? THIS IS WHAT YOU'RE DOING SITTING HERE? I WONDERED WHY THERE WAS AN EMPTY TABLE AND A HUGE LINE OF MONSTERS. LISTEN, YOU'RE KINDA COOL AND EVERYTHIN BUT MY GHOULFRIEND WOULI UNLEASH A THOUSAND EVIL CURSES ON ME IF I EVER CHEATED ON HER.

D

Wow, oh, I can't believe I'm here at this event, with you and, like, this isn't normally the kind of thing I get to do, but ever since Frankie brought me to life as her fake boyfriend I've been looking for a creeperific ghoul to hang out with, can you pick me, pleeeease?

E

HEY, GHOUL, YOU'RE LOOKING SCARY-COOL. WANT SOME HOT STUFF TO WARM THE PLACE WHERE YOUR ICY HEART SHOULD BE? IF SO, CALL OFF YOUR SEARCH. I AM THE HOTTEST MONSTER AT MONSTER HIGH. I'M ALSO THE FASTEST. WHAT? CLAWDEEN BEAT ME? THAT'S JUST A RUMOUR! ANYWAY, DON'T BE AN ICE QUEEN, LET THE MOST UGHSOME MONSTER IN SCHOOL THAW YOU OUT!

F

UGHGHHH, EERRRRR, YUGGGG, UGGGGGGG, EEEEEEERGH, GHOULIA, UGHHHHH, ARRGHHHH, EEEEEERM.

CLAWD WOLF

HOODUDE VOODOO

DEUCE GORGON

HOLT HYDE

HEATH BURNS

SLO MO

The Monster Wish List

Hey ghoulfriend! Don't know about you, but we can't wait to find out what spooktastic shocks and creeperific surprises the next year has in store for Monster High! Think about the next year of your monster life and use this page to write down all your hopes and wishes – from learning a scary-cool skill to throwing an ughsome party. Here's hoping all your screams come true!

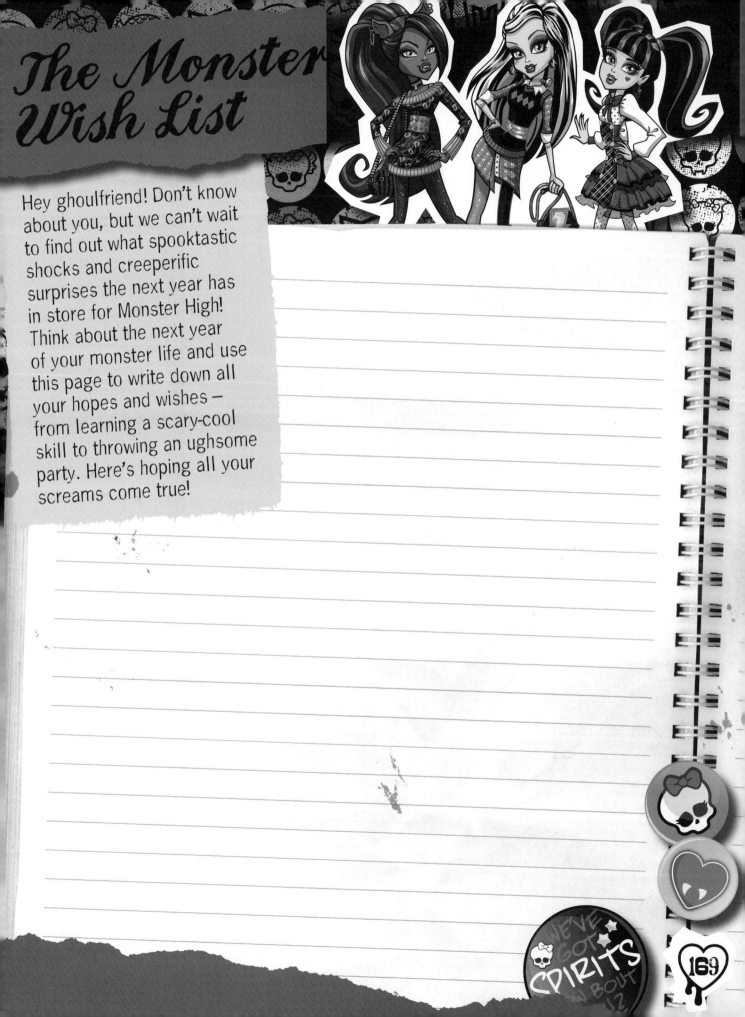

FEEL THE FEAR

The spooktacular grimnasium is the scene of Monster High's major sporting triumphs. Our casketball team, led by Deuce, regularly thrashes other schools on this court! We also hold fearleading practice here. Right now Cleo's looking for some new recruits. Interested?

If you want to impress Cleo, you'll need to pull out all of the stops! There are eight scary-cool frames on this page. Use them to plot out your very own monster cheer routine! Think up a clawsome set of steps, then draw one move into each panel. Good luck!

POSTER GHOULS

Okay, your cheer was not totally dreadful. I might give you a place on the fear squad if you can draw a poster for our upcoming fearleading competition. It's taking place in the grimnasium, on Halloween, at midnight. Make sure it looks totally golden!

Pick out your favourite pens and start designing! Cleo's team needs a poster that will get Monster High's fearleading fans flocking to the grim — think fierce, fly and freaky on the eye. Oh. My. Ra!

Psychic Scarah

Scarah Screams has a terror-ific talent – she can hear other monsters' thoughts! Test your own psychic power by matching these wicked wonderings to the monster who's thinking them.

1

2

3

4

5

A

Oh my Ra! If I don't get the lead part in the school play, I'm going to unravel!

B

I am not understanding this way of falling head over the heels for boys.

C

Why can't every monster at school just put their empty cans in the recycling bin?

D

MAN, CLEO IS AWESOME, BUT TONIGHT I REALLY WANT TO HANG OUT WITH MY BROS.

E

DON'T SET THIS BOOK ON FIRE, DON'T SET THIS BOOK ON FIRE....

THIS IS MY MONSTER high!

Imagine you're a student at Monster High!
Who would be in your skeleton crew?
Fill in your freaky-fab facts below.

**MY SKELETON CREW
WOULD INCLUDE:**

I'D BE CRUSHING ON:
(add a sticker of your
monster crush)

**MY FAVOURITE
ACTIVITY WOULD BE:**

MY MONSTER STYLE WOULD BE:
(draw a picture of yourself)

**MY BEAST FRIEND
WOULD BE:**
(add a sticker of your fave ghoul)

**THE CLASSES I WOULD
LIKE BEST WOULD BE:**

goodBye
FROM
MONSTER
HIGH!

173

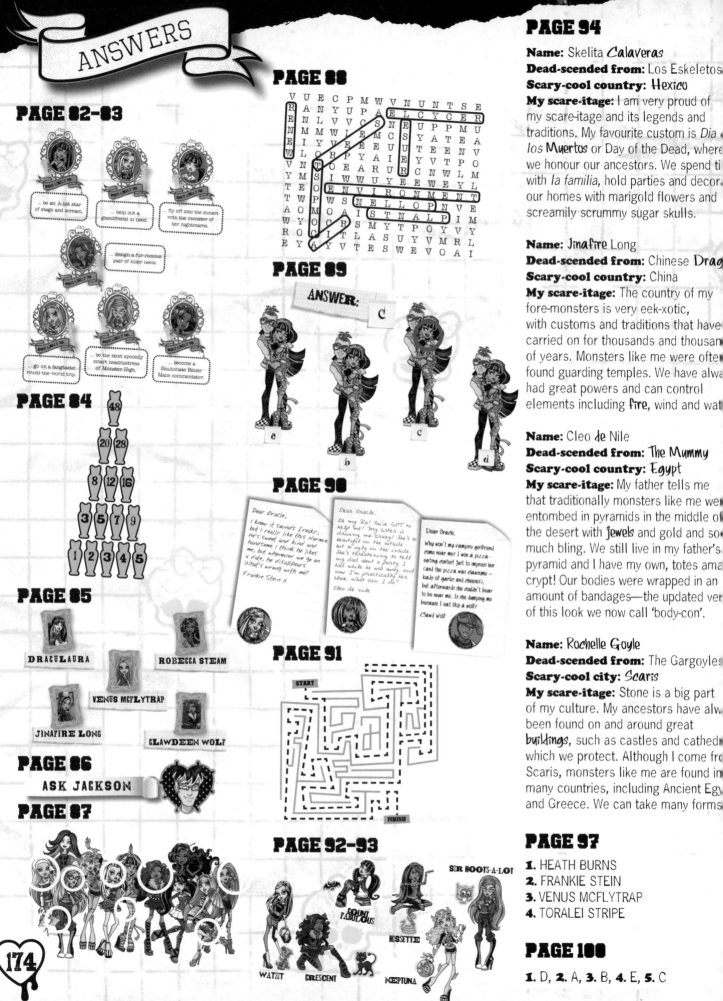

ANSWERS

PAGE 82-83

... be an A-list star of stage and scream.

... help out a ghoulfriend in need.

... fly off into the sunset with the monster of her nightmares.

... design a fur-rocious pair of killer heels.

... go on a fangtastic round-the-world trip.

... be the next spookily smart headmistress of Monster High.

... become a Skultimate Roller Maze commentator.

PAGE 84

48

20 28

8 12 16

3 5 7 9

1 2 3 4 5

PAGE 85

DRACULAURA

ROBECCA STEAM

VENUS MCFLYTRAP

JINAFIRE LONG

CLAWDEEN WOLF

PAGE 86

ASK JACKSON

PAGE 87

PAGE 88

V U E C P M W A V N U N T S E
R E N E W U P A C E L C Y C E R
A M I L M Y O P N E U P P M U A
N M E V U E S M C U R E S U R E
W L Y T O W P E A C R C N W L L
E W Y T A R Y U A R U T E E N P
W Y T A M E O Y S T R C W E Y L
T T M E O Y W E A R V E N V E A
A W R O Y W O A I R O N M E N T
W R O Y A R W S N E L L O P N V E
R E O Y A I S T N A L P I V I
E Y S M Y T P S M Y T P O Y V L
T L A S U Y V M R L
T E S W E V O A I

PAGE 89

ANSWER: c

a   b   c   d

PAGE 90

Dear Oracle,
I know it sounds freaky, but I really like this Normie. He's sweet and kind and handsome. I think he likes me, but whenever we go on a date, he disappears. What's wrong with me?
Frankie Stein X

Dear Oracle,
Oh my Ra! You've GOT to help me! My sister is driving me crazy! She's so beautiful on the outside but so ugly on the inside. She's threatening to tell my dad about a party I held while he was away, and now I'm practically her slave. what can I do?
Cleo de nile

Dear Oracle,
Why won't my vampire girlfriend come near me? I won a pizza-eating contest just to impress her (and the pizza was clawsome – loads of garlic and cheese!), but afterwards she couldn't bear to be near me. Is she dumping me because I eat like a wolf?
Clawd Wolf

PAGE 91

START

FINISH

PAGE 92-93

SIR HOOTS-A-LOT

COUNT FABULOUS

HISSETTE

WATZIT   CRESCENT   NEPTUNA

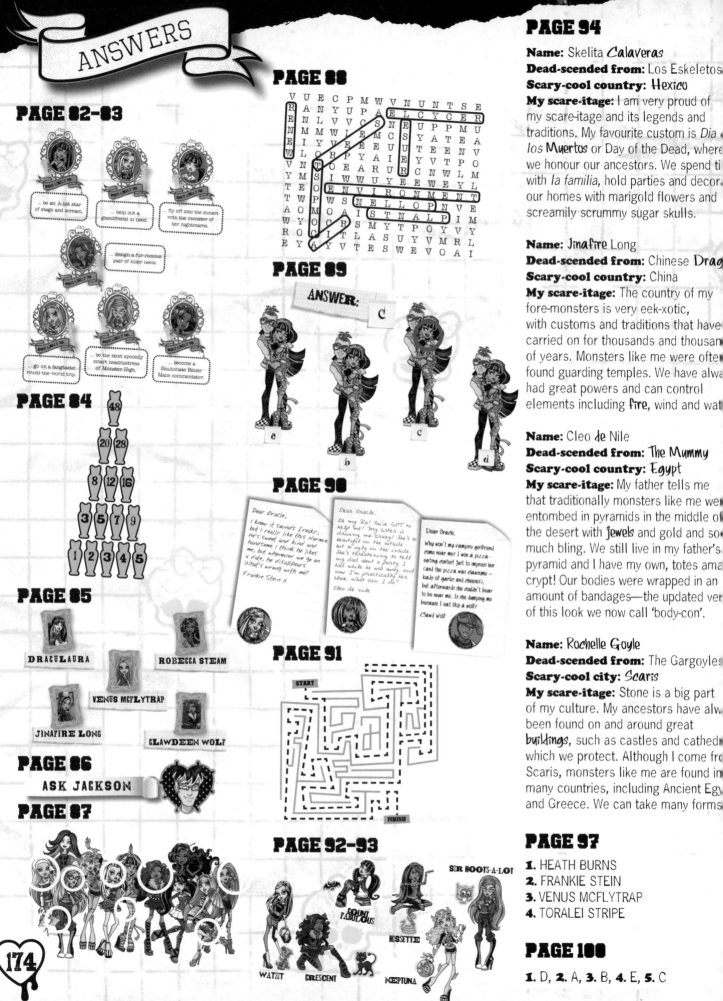

PAGE 94

Name: Skelita Calaveras
Dead-scended from: Los Eskeletos
Scary-cool country: Hexico
My scare-itage: I am very proud of my scare-itage and its legends and traditions. My favourite custom is *Dia los Muertos* or Day of the Dead, where we honour our ancestors. We spend ti with *la familia*, hold parties and decor our homes with marigold flowers and screamily scrummy sugar skulls.

Name: Jinafire Long
Dead-scended from: Chinese Drag
Scary-cool country: China
My scare-itage: The country of my fore-monsters is very eek-xotic, with customs and traditions that have carried on for thousands and thousan of years. Monsters like me were ofte found guarding temples. We have alwa had great powers and can control elements including fire, wind and wat

Name: Cleo de Nile
Dead-scended from: The Mummy
Scary-cool country: Egypt
My scare-itage: My father tells me that traditionally monsters like me wer entombed in pyramids in the middle of the desert with jewels and gold and so much bling. We still live in my father's pyramid and I have my own, totes ama crypt! Our bodies were wrapped in an amount of bandages—the updated ver of this look we now call 'body-con'.

Name: Rochelle Goyle
Dead-scended from: The Gargoyles
Scary-cool city: Scaris
My scare-itage: Stone is a big part of my culture. My ancestors have alwa been found on and around great buildings, such as castles and cathedr which we protect. Although I come fro Scaris, monsters like me are found in many countries, including Ancient Egy and Greece. We can take many forms

PAGE 97

1. HEATH BURNS
2. FRANKIE STEIN
3. VENUS MCFLYTRAP
4. TORALEI STRIPE

PAGE 100

1. D, **2.** A, **3.** B, **4.** E, **5.** C

174

AGE 102

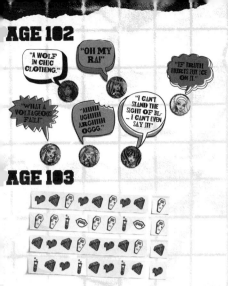

"A WOLF IN CHIC CLOTHING."

"OH MY RA!"

"IF TRUTH HURTS PUT ICE ON IT."

"WHAT A VOLTAGEOUS FAIL!"

"AIIII! UGIHIII ARGHIIII OGGG."

"I CAN'T STAND THE SIGHT OF BL... I CAN'T EVEN SAY IT!"

AGE 103

AGE 104-105

. FALSE – Skelita is from Hexico.

. TRUE

. TRUE

. FALSE – she's a famous pop star.

. TRUE – but she wants to help normies, not
 care them!

. FALSE – Meowlody is Purrsephone's twin.

. FALSE – not after a millennia inside a lamp!

. TRUE – she's a purr-fect artist.

. TRUE

. FALSE – her boy is Clawd Wolf!

AGE 106

START

FINISH

AGE 107

AGE 108

owleen has a crush on Romulus.

AGE 109

2	5	4	6	1	3
5	1	3	2	5	4
1	4	2	3	6	5
6	3	6	4	2	1
4	2	1	5	3	6
3	6	5	1	4	2

PAGE 110-111

PAGE 112

The alien invaders are 3 and 7.

1. SPECTRA VONDERGEIST

2. CATTY NOIR

3. ALIEN INVADER

4. VENUS MCFLYTRAP

5. JINAFIRE LONG

6. SKELITA CALAVERAS

7. FAKE STUDENT

8. DEUCE GORGON

PAGE 113

Line 1 leads to Deuce

Line 3 leads to Cleo

Line 4 leads to Gil

Line 7 leads to Abbey

Line 8 leads to Jinafire

Line 9 leads to Clawdeen

PAGE 116

1. Slo Mo

2. Howleen Wolf

3. Draculaura

4. Cleo de Nile herself!

PAGE 117

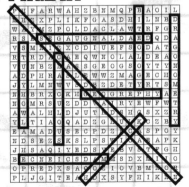

PAGE 118-119

Captain Penny

Shiver

Rhuen

Roux

Chewlian

Perseus

PAGE 121

1. Jinafire Long, **2.** Sunglasses, **3.** Eiffel Tower,
4. Rochelle and Jinafire, **5.** No, the far right,
6. Rochelle Goyle, **7.** Skelita Calaveras

PAGE 125

1. Clawd Wolf, **2.** Sunglasses,
3. Boots, **4.** On the left,
5. Flowers, **6.** Three, **7.** No,
8. Three, including Clawd's

PAGE 126

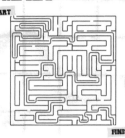

START

FINISH

PAGE 127

The mischievous kitty is MEOWLODY

N	H	Y	D	O	L	W	O	E	M	T	S	X
N	E	O	P	U	R	R	S	E	M	O	P	H
I	P	C	L	A	D	W	O	L	S	F	O	E
E	I	F	E	T	O	R	A	L	E	O	L	A
T	R	R	C	R	H	Y	D	A	D	O	C	T
S	T	A	L	S	O	Y	O	U	S	D	N	H
E	S	S	A	T	T	O	D	S	L	U	O	B
I	I	I	W	E	I	E	N	E	O	D	M	U
K	E	M	D	U	V	E	I	H	M	O	I	R
N	L	O	W	O	N	G	Y	M	O	A	S	N
A	A	C	O	J	N	R	O	M	I	L	A	S
R	R	D	L	M	A	N	N	Y	T	A	U	R
F	O	A	F	R	A	K	I	E	R	R	S	H
O	T	S	U	L	U	M	O	R	H	O	K	T

PAGE 130-131

Can't Fight the Moonlight – Clawdeen Wolf

A Vampire's Kiss Is Just A Kiss – Draculaura

Egyptian Allure – Cleo de Nile

Enchantment Under The Sea – Lagoona Blue

Catacomb Chaos – Robecca Steam

Midnight In Scaris – Rochelle Goyle

Graveyard Glitz – Spectra Vondergeist

Winter Wonderland – Abbey Bominable

Green Scream – Venus McFlytrap

Time Of My Unlife – Frankie Stein

PAGE 133

1. Yeti, **2.** c – Transylvania,
3. Pyramids, **4.** a – Silver,
5. False (she turned her hair into snakes),
6. Scotland.

PAGE 134-135

ANSWERS

PAGE 136-137

1. B, **2.** Casketball, **3.** HOME ICK,
4. All of them – Frankie's currents cause problems in the water, Rochelle sinks like a stone, and there is a large octo-creature lurking in the caves beneath the pool!
5. Mr Hackington, **6.** Mr Rotter,
7. The catacombs, **8.** In their coffin lockers,
9. True (although Lagoona sometimes smuggles in Neptuna, her pet piranha, in her water-filled bag), **10.** Nightmare, **11.** C, **12.** A,
13. They are all extra-scare-icular activities at Monster High

PAGE 138-139

A. Mr D'eath, **B.** Cleo de Nile,
C. Spectra Vondergeist, **D.** HooDude Voodoo,
E. Ms Kindergrübber, **F.** Venus McFlytrap

PAGE 140-141

1. Abbey Bominable, **2.** Draculaura,
3. Cleo de Nile, **4.** Jackson Jekyll

PAGE 142

1. D, **2.** C, **3.** E, **4.** A, **5.** B

PAGE 143

1. Abbey Bominable, **2.** Jinafire Long,
3. Toralei Stripe, **4.** Clawd Wolf,
5. Skelita Calaveras, **6.** Venus McFlytrap,
7. HooDude Voodoo, **8.** Draculaura

PAGE 146

1. EERIE MEANIE by Justin Biter
2. BITE ME MAYBE by Scary Rah Jeepers
3. SINGLE ZOMBIES (PUT A RING ON IT) by Beetlebouncé
4. GHOUL GIRL STYLE by Psychotic
5. MONSTERAZZI by Lady Ghoula
6. WE ARE NEVER EVER FANGING OUT TOGETHER by Terror Swift
7. JUST THE WAY WE HOWL by the Jaundice Brothers
8. HE WOLF by Shriekeera
9. CHILLER by Frightful Jackson
10. THE FEARSOME PHANTOM OF THE OPERA THEME (REMIX) by Crescenda von Hammerstone

PAGE 151

PAGE 152

1. TRUE, **2.** FALSE, **3.** FALSE, **4.** TRUE,
5. TRUE, **6.** FALSE, **7.** TRUE. **8.** FALSE,
9. TRUE, **10.** TRUE

PAGE 153

PAGE 154

PAGE 158-159

Spectra's words:
Violet, Angel Cake, Curious, Persistent, Floating, Transparent, Ghostly Gossip, Journalism, Haunting, Chains, Pale, Kind, Rhuen, Rattle, Silk, Defensive, Ferret.

Rochelle's words:
Rock Candy, Iron, Stained Glass, Griffin, Protective, Architecture, Grey, Sculpting, Roux, Scaris, Pigeons, Disgruntled.

PAGE 160-161

PAGE 162

PAGE 165

The extra word is CHLORINE.

S	M	I	W	S	I	M	I	N	G	U	O
A	N	T	E	N	I	R	O	L	H	C	L
L	P	R	E	T	A	W	H	S	E	R	F
T	T	O	T	V	A	N	O	A	P	J	S
W	U	S	U	S	E	A	N	S	R	F	W
A	W	E	L	N	B	O	H	S	I	F	F
T	C	V	E	L	G	E	T	U	N	E	I
E	L	A	V	R	I	T	I	S	D	R	N
R	O	W	A	G	O	G	D	I	U	A	S
S	R	P	S	E	V	W	E	T	E	R	E
R	H	S	N	E	P	T	U	N	E	G	F
Y	S	A	E	D	M	J	V	T	N	G	I

PAGE 168

A. Holt Hyde
B. Clawd Wolf
C. Deuce Gorgon
D. HooDude Voodoo
E. Heath Burns
F. Slo Mo

PAGE 172

1. B, **2.** D, **3.** C, **4.** E, **5.** A

TERROR-IFIC TALES

Unlife To Live

Ghoulia Yelps was studying on the school steps when....

Ghoulia, we're going for smoothies in free period, want to join us?

O.M.Ra! You're too busy, you're sitting there like do every day!

Nurrgh!

Suddenly a brain-shaped distress signal lit up the sky. Ghoulia sprang into action....

Ghoulia whisked the Headmistress to the salon and back....

Ghoulia! I need to get my hair done for the Superintendent's party tonight, but I'm swamped with paperwork....

Thanks Ghoulia, I look fabulous!

Next, there was an icy issue at the pool....

Is yours now.

Crikey, it's ffffreezing!

Doom At GLOOM BEACH

The ghouls were dissecting what they'd packed for their trip to Gloom Beach....

Ten pairs of flats, nine boots, eight sandals....

Is that enough?

But Cleo had more than fashion on her mind....

I hope you've saved room in there for your fearleading uniforms ... we have to win Gloom Beach Spirit Staff

It was a long journey and while the girls slept and dreamed....

How about a little song?

At last they arrived....

A ghoul could get used to this!

It's even beautiful I imagin

Unfortunately their cabin wasn't quite what they'd been expecting....

It's not exactly the Four Screamons.

It's not that bad....

It's a dump!

THE END

The Comic Clubbers, led by die-hard graphics-freak Ghoulia Yelps, have taken a lurk back at Monster High hiss-tory. Did you know that the school's unique student bodies didn't always skelebrate each other's differences?

Hiss-toria

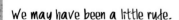
Werewolf and vampire high schools have been at each other's throats for a thousand years....

Gggggggggrrrrrr!

It can be said that the war ended here, at Monster High.

We transferred from an all-vampire school. It wasn't easy....

Vampires like Bram Devein and Gory Fangtell were new to Monster High.

Mwah Ha Ha Ha Ha!

Eeuurgh! You smell. Maybe it's time to use soap and water ... instead of your tongues.

Vampires made cutting comments to the werewolves....

We may have been a little rude.

We werewolves weren't any better....

This is our turf now, got it vam-poseurs?

Ha Ha Ha Haoooooooowl!

The werewolves got aggressive ...

Garlic totally gives vampires mega monster zits!

... and mean to the vampires!

Aaaaargh! Garlic! Run for it!

It was so voltagiously intense!

The smallest thing could set off a major battle....

This bathroom is now for vampires only.

You can't do that!

Did I see you growl at this vampire? Don't forget your place!

Grrrrrrrrr!

The atmosphere was horrifically tense!

The gym, sundown, bring your full strength!

Agreed. We can't go on like this!

Things hit breaking point.

But in time the vampires and werewolves realized that....

At Monster High what makes us unique brings us together, and together we can conquer the real enemy – prejudice!

Now vampire-werewolf relations have never been better!

Clawd, all I'm saying is you could have called me!

So now I howl too loud!?

You could have howled. Like when you're watching casketball and I'm trying to study!

You're cute when you're angry.

See!

THE END

187

Bean Scare, Done That

It was time for the fear squad's charity fundraiser at the Maul....

Where are you ghouls going?

To the Coffin Bean, to work for free.

I hold the record for the most money raised!

Until today!

The proceeds were going to an awesome children's charity.

The challenge was on

The ghouls soon had their first customers....

This will keep track of all the money we raise!

We have to beat Nefera's record.

I'll have a small sugar-free vanilla fangoccino.

A monster triple espresso with chocolate sprinkles....

Things were going scarily well.

Looks like your record's going to need bandages, Nefera.

I like to call this Cleo's bad luck charm.

The ghouls were on track to smash Nefera's total, until....

Doubt that!

Nefera pulled out one of her father's cursed idols.

188

TOUGH AS SCALES

In the lie-bury there are many ancient books, including the Monster High-clopedia, which details the many lessons the student bodies have learned as they pass through the school. Here are two such tales....

One day in metalwork class....

Killer job on the stand, Jinafire

The fire-breathing daughter of the Chinese Dragon had welded a mount for the winning casketball.

This ball's irreplaceable!

Careful, Flame-brain!

But while the guys were arguing ...

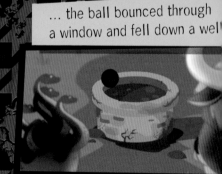

... the ball bounced through a window and fell down a well

Jinafire led the boys underground to find it.

Step aside. Let Manny show ya how it's done!

The boys were sure they could reach the ball.

We need to calculate the distance down and then ...

Activities planned.

Wool Collecting Club, Rock and Pebble Society.....

This is what you guys do for fun?

I heard so much spook-takular stuff about Monster High, but none of it's true!

Rider was horrified!

Frankie ran Rider through the most boring clubs at Monster High.

I may have told him that Scream is the most epic thing you can possibly do!

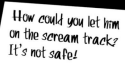

Whooooo-hoooo!

The ghouls looked everywhere for Rider.

Then Toralei slyly admitted she'd directed Rider towards the scream track.

Sure enough, Rider was burning rubber in the grim.

How could you let him on the scream track? It's not safe!

Maybe he knows better than us what he can and can't do!

raculaura rounded on Clawd.

The werewolf told the ghouls that they were being over-protective.

Suddenly there was a crash!

The ghouls ran to check that Rider was OK....

This is who I am. If I need help, I'll ask. Cool?

Yeah.

Rider just wasn't a sit-around kinda dude!

That was totally spin-sane!!! I'm going again!

Rider reminded Frankie that she'd said he could be himself at Monster High.

Will you light my wheels on fire? I wanna try this again!

THE END

193

Frankie Stein can't stand injustice at Monster High, but is she the beast candidate for Student Disembodied President?

One monstrous morning at Monster High …

Can you zombies move any slower?!

… some zombies were causing tailbacks in the coffin corridor.

Poor zombies! They need their own lane in the hall.

The ghouls couldn't help feeling sorry for their slow-moving schoolmates.

Suddenly Frankie had a high-voltage brainwave.

STUDENT DISEMBODIED PRESIDENT

I'm gonna run for Student Disembodied President, then I'll help them.

So the ghouls got to work promoting their GFF.

FRANKIE'S GHOUL

Cleo even agreed to be Frankie's campaign manager.

Frankie soon found their help came with strings attached….

You'll make my birthday a school holiday, right?

She thought things couldn't get more horrific …

I just want you to lose.

TORALEI FOR PURRSIDENT

…. then she discovered Toralei was running against her.

Nevertheless, at Stein HQ, the ghouls were determined to help Frankie to victory.

STEIN HEADQUARTERS

VOTE FOR ME

Draculaura was making slogan tees, while Ghoulia was getting ready to record the campaign commercial …

I SHINE FOR FRANKIE STEIN

…. directed by Cleo of course!

TAKE 001 **SCENE** 001

DIRECTOR Cleo De Nile

Yes, I hate creepateria food!

Frankie explained her message….

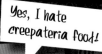

"Yes, I know how werewolves feel on the full moon."

"But what really leaves a bad taste in my mouth is our poor treatment of zombies."

The ghouls went off to dr[...] for Frankie, so they didn't [...] sneakily fire-up Ghoulia's [...]

Later that day.....

"Frankie! Look!"

Toralei had sent her edited version of Frankie's film to everyone in school. It sounded as if Frankie hated werewolves and bad-mouthed zombies!

There was no time to [...] anything about Toralei[...] The debate was on.

"You should hear from someone who has experienced injustice first hand."

"Poor thing!"

The student bodies were moved to tears.

"Snnnifffff!"

"This breaks my heart."

Frankie explained she was running to give zombies a voice.

DEBAT[...]

The audience burst [...] applause as Franki[...] them to stand with [...]

No one was surprised by the election result — except Toralei!

"I told everyone to vote for Slow Moe. He's the best voice for the zombies."

Slow Moe was Student Disembodied President.

"So ... about making my birthday a school holiday?"

ELECTION RESULTS

67%

33%

0%

"You did the right thing!"

"Lucky him!"

Scarah-voyant

When Scarah Screams sets her sights on dating InvisiBilly it takes some monster matchmaking from her fiends to make it happen....

The ghouls were fanging out in the coffin corridor ...

... when Scarah Screams came walking by.

Hey Scarah, what number am I thinking of?

Frankie loved testing Scarah's psychic skills ...

I don't know ... one - the loneliest number?

... but today Scarah seemed somewhat out of sorts.

All right Scarah, which boy has you all wrapped up?

Buzz Wingman?

Golden ghoul Cleo knew exactly what the problem was.

Scarah admitted it was InvisiBilly she liked.

Draculaura told him everything.

Draculaura suggested Scarah go and talk to him ...

If I get too close I'd hear what he's thinking, What if I heard he doesn't like me?

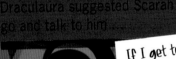

But she didn't dare.

'ssup?

Just then Clawd turned up.

Well, InvisiBilly and Scarah would make a perfect couple except she's too shy and Billy's too quiet and ...

Clawd promised to talk to Billy.

Clawd caught up with Billy in the creepateria.

I heard about you and Scarah.

What did you hear?

That you like her.

But Billy had the same doubts as Scarah.

I'm afraid that if I get too close she'll read my mind and see I like her and that might freak her out.

I can't!

You gotta be transparent with her.

Luckily Frankie came up with a brilliant idea ...

Oooh! I think I know how to fix this.

... which used Scarah's mind-reading abilities.

The Stitchuation

There's a handsome new guy trotting the howlways of Monster High! He's got Operetta and Toralei in a spooky spin....

Spectra was on the steps of Monster High writing her blog.

Time for the Ghostly Gossip to tell the ghouls what's hot and what's not....

Hold your horses, look at the Mustang that just pulled up!

Suddenly a handsome centaur trotted past.

Frankie was excited by the news.

A new boy!

Oh no! More competition!

Jackson Jekyll was not!

Huh? Wow!

Within seconds Spectra had updated her blog.

Frankie's bolts fizzed with volts as the handsome half-horse passed by.

But she wasn't the only ghoul with her eye on the new boy.

Operetta couldn't wait to make her move.

Well hey, sugar. Fancy meeting a colt like you in a school like this.

But the gorgeous centaur just kept walking.

Toralei was full of scorn.

Oh what a clumsy kitty.

Aaargh!

Nice try, country mouse. Let me show you how it's done.

She approached Archer and

... but instead of helping her, Archer

CLAWBACKS

When both Cleo and Toralei vie for the lead in the school production of *The Wizard Of Ooze* all howl breaks loose.

It was school production time at Monster High ...

Hey Cleo!

Toralei, I barely saw you there. I mean you're just sooo forgettable!

... and claws were out on the coffin corridor.

You've got no chance at getting the lead role.

I was born to play Gore-athy in *The Wizard Of Ooze!*

The fight for the lead role was on!

You're older than the pyramids ... this is a part for a young monster, like me! Good luck – grandmummy!

Toralei had the last catty meow.

Grandmummy? Wait ... that's it!

This gave Cleo an idea.

My grandmummy!

In her locker was a bottle of potion her grandmummy had given her.

Looking at the bottle she heard her grandmummy's words....

In this bottle is magical water from the fountain of youth!

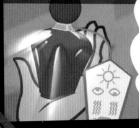

Gore-athy is as good as mine!

She dabbed the potion on her neck.

On stage the newly youthful Cleo gave the audition of her life.

Mr Where was stunned.

Outstanding Cleo, so vibrant, such enthusiasm!

Toralei, however, wasn't so easily impressed.

There's something seriously fishy going on with that ghoul!

Toralei watched from the rafters as Cleo doused herself in youth potion.

I knew it!

Toralei!

The furious kitty leapt down and confronted her rival.

Paws off!

Give me some!

A cat-fight ensued.

What's going on?

They are acting like hungry yaks at meal time.

Frankie and Abbey looked on in surprise ...

I need to be younger! No, I need to be younger!

... as the silly ghouls fought over the bottle ...

... which flew into the air and soaked them both in potion!

The magical glow eventually faded to reveal two tiny beings.

Oh no! We're monster babies.

The monster babies were not happy!

I'm sure there's some kind of reversal ... right?

... and Clawbacks are in two minutes!

There was nothing the ghouls could do but go on stage for their clawbacks as babies.

She cursed me with her crazy potion.

Mr Where, I can explain....

Yes, but my grandmummy has to send it to me ...

Wahhh!

You should have just let go!

Luckily Mr Where had good news for the ghouls.

You are perfect for the part!

Huh? Is it me?

Which one?

... with two teeny tiny co-stars.

We represent the crawly-tot guild.

On performance night, the curtains opened to reveal Venus McFlytrap as Gore-athy ...

The crunchkins!

Fierce Crush

Howleen Wolf finds out that love can be furrociously tricky when she falls for an older werewolf....

It was the first full moon of the Lunar Leap Year....

Wear my ring?

... and romance was in the air.

My Clawsity Jacket?

Oh Clawd!

Wear my flea collar?

Everyone was feeling loved....

Everyone, that is, except Howleen.

Don't go fallin' into that 'I gotta get a boyfriend' trap!

Clawdeen told Howleen she was way too young for boys.

I'm not, I'm not, I'm not, I'M NOT!!!!

Hi Rom!

... and gallantly opened Howleen's rusty locker.

Just then Romulus came over...

Wow!

You are barking up the wrong tree sis — he used to puppy-sit you!

That night ...

... the students gathered for Full Moon Sports Day.

Welcome to Monster High's Full Moon Sports Day!

Yay Team!

Howleen took the opportunity to open up to her friend.

I really like him Lothar.

Did Romulus like her, too?

Lothar knew just what unrequited love was like!

He had it bad for Howleen.

But Howleen just didn't notice.

How can I make him notice me?

Do the things he likes to do.

She was too wrapped up in Romulus!

Howleen knew Romulus liked sticks ...

Hey, those are for the bonfire!

... so she borrowed one.

She threw it for Romulus.

Sadly, it was shaped like a boomerang.

It soared straight back towards the fire ...

No!

Not this way!

... and Romulus followed.

Howleen had no choice but to douse him with water.

Are you ok?

FIELD OF SCREAMS

Who's ready for some voltagious fun?

Toralei and the Werecat twins have a purr-fect plan for stopping the ghouls beating them in the corn maze race ... or do they?

Dawn broke in the grounds of Monster High.

Frankie and her fiends headed for the corn maze.

Frankie had the map.

Everyone seemed unsure.

A race through a maze?

Then Gil Webber piped up.

Who's in the lead now?

I do not 'race' anywhere!

The winning team gets their picture in *The Gory Gazette!*

The scheming kitty rocked up to gloat!

Your record is history!

They looked at the scoreboard ... Toralei!

You flea-brains really think you're going to beat our time?

They entered the vast, spooky maze …

… but it wasn't long before they were lost.

Left does look shorter!

What do you think, Lagoona?

Heath got hungry.

Popcorn, anyone?

He decided to pop some corn himself …

… accidentally setting fire to the map.

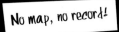

HEATH!!!!

Whatever.....

No map, no record!

How would they win now?

I hope we can find our way out!

Perched in a tree, Toralei grinned devilishly.

We've been wandering around here forever!

It's been four minutes, love.

Suddenly, Manny Taur thundered past.

207

Finally, some luck!

He's a minotaur! They're bonza at mazes – he can lead us out!

Toralei threw corn on the path …

Hey!

What…?

… which attracted flocks of crows.

Into the path of Toralei …

Go, get 'em boys!

… who released some wild beasts.

I'm the only one in my family that stinks at mazes.

The minotaur admitted

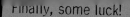

They followed Manny.

Luckily they could still see Manny's hoofprints.

Now the ghouls had devil hounds on their tail.

… and that he was frightened by 'scary things' in the maze.

Manny was running so fast…

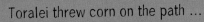

… he didn't notice Toralei with arms of corn.

The gang followed the trail.

Suddenly they came upon Manny, crying.

Run!!!!

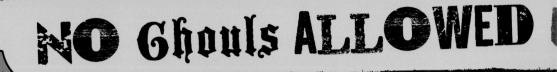

NO Ghouls ALLOWED

When Clawd Wolf suddenly cancels his date with Draculaura she smells a rat! Just what does 'Guys' Night Out' involve?

Draculaura was freaked out.

I can't make it tonight. I'm ... er ... studying with Romulus.

Clawd had cancelled their date.

The cute vampire told her ghoulfriends what had happened.

Clawd and Deuce promised to help Mr Hack repaint his hearse.

No! They're all going to Gil's to work on that rap album.

They soon realized the boys were up to something.

But what exactly?

Look, tonight is our guys' night out....

No ghouls allowed.

They decided to find out just what the guys had planned so they ...

... intercepted notes ...

The guys had been angrily talking about 'battle strategy', leading the ghouls to a horrible conclusion....

... eavesdropped ...

... and even did some underwater surveillance.

They're going to fight!

They tracked the guys to a graveyard and peeped over the stones.

Were the guys really fighting?

Level 4 lasers, right through your defences!

In fact, 'Guys' Night' involved a very nerdy game!

Boys are so weird ... but they're adorable!

This is hilarious!

The ghouls decided to make a night of it!

THE END

Tortoise & the Scare

Shuffling zombie Ghoulia Yelps may not be the freaky-fastest ghoul in school, but she sure is scary smart. So what happened when Monster High's mean ghoul Toralei Stripe challenged Ghoulia to a race?

One day in the coffin corridor, Ghoulia tapped Toralei on the shoulder.

Hey! She was just trying to invite you to her party!

She was trying to be nice!

Whatever it is, make it fast ... oh wait, you can't, you're a zombie.

Clawdeen, Frankie and the ghouls overheard and stuck up for their friend.

But Toralei carried on making fun of zombies.

To prove her point, Toralei challenged Ghoulia to a race across school.

The ghouls tried to think of ways to help their friend ...

We could get Toralei to chase this laser pointer down the wrong hall. ...

Let me guess, it starts at eight, but the zombies don't get there 'til eleven!

If you win, I'll serve food at your party. If I win, you serve at one of mine!

This is cheating!

I can hit her with pies! Be pretty funny. ...

Toralei was so confident she'd win she even stopped to boast.

... but Frankie thought Ghoulia should rise to the challenge alone.

Meanwhile in the catacombs, Ghoulia was busy tickling the dragon's nostrils until ...

Aaatchoooo

By the time Toralei sauntered into class. ...

I've got a purr-fect headline for your Ghostly Gossip blog - 'Zombies Serve Kitties At High-End Soirée!'

Wha...? What? How?

... the beast sneezed her right across school!

Clever Ghoulia was hard at work.

... waitress Toralei had to eat her words ...

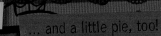

... and a little pie, too!

Later, while Ghoulia threw some shapes on the dance floor at her party ...

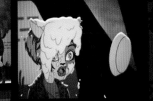

THE END

Tree of Unlife

Can Venus McFlytrap's dead-ication to her environmental cause save the oldest living tree at Monster High?

Venus had her tendrils in a twist.

Cleo! Huge emergency!

Careful! They're designer!

She needed some bandages from Cleo's spare stash.

As Venus sped off, Lagoona showed up ...

You seen Venus? She told me to bring her 3,000 cc of distilled water...

... followed by Frankie and Abbey.

She told us to bring the largest thermometer we could find.

What was Venus up to?

The ghouls found Venus with a very sick tree.

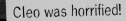

Hang in there, big guy!

First she used Abbey's thermometer to take the tree's temperature.

Quick! We don't have much time!

Then she used Lagoona's water on the tree's roots.

Cleo was horrified!

Ohhh! My Ghostier bandages!!!

Venus explained the severity of the situation.

Cleo! This is the oldest living tree at Monster High. He's been here for hundreds of years.

What wrong with it — er ... I mean him?

Venus sobbed that the precious tree was dying.

I've tried everything....

Someone must know what to do ... a teacher, a scientist?

"Mother Nature! She'll know."

She asked Mother Nature's advice about the Great Oak.

Venus led the ghouls to a secret lake.

"Remember what the tree has been to you...."

"Call Cleo and tell her to get every monster in school out by the tree, ASAP!"

Cleo did as Venus asked.

Mother Nature told them love the tree back to life.

"Why are we standing by the overgrown piece of firewood?"

Everyone gathered around the sick tree.

Venus explained the tree was a living history of themselves.

Frankie reminded Ghoulia she used to study by the tree.

The tree may have been sick, but he still didn't like being insulted.

"I wrote some of my best stories under this tree."

"Uggrr huhh!"

"I lost five soccer balls in its branches."

The zombie gave the Oak a nostalgic squeeze.

"And Clawd and I came here on our first date — see?"

Soon everyone was sharing memories.

The student bodies had loved the tree back to full health.

With every lovely memory, more leaves sprouted on the tree's branches.

"Look!"

Until....

It was time for a creeperific celebration!

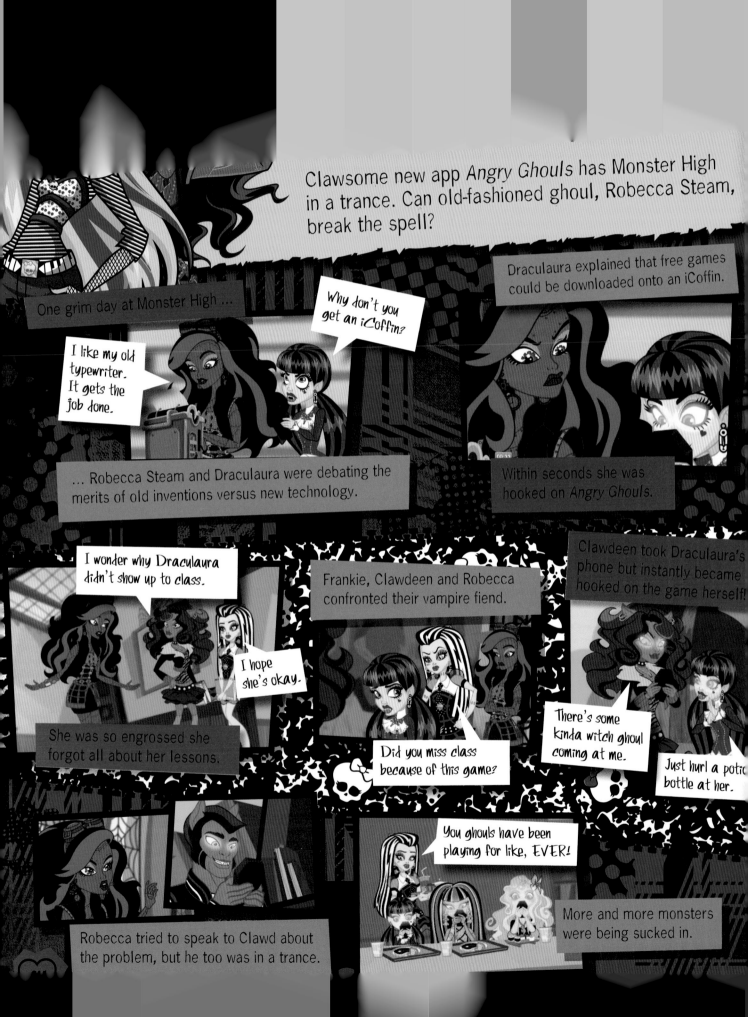

Even sensible Frankie succumbed to the lure of *Angry Ghouls*.

Ooooh!

Mr Rotter was not amused to find Frankie playing games in class.

You can pick up your little gadget from Miss Bloodgood's office later.

Oh! What an interesting looking game.

Soon everyone's grades began to slip.

Look, new high score!

Robecca was steaming mad!

It seemed she was the only monster unimpressed by the game.

When Mr Hack was so distracted he let an experiment explode, Robecca knew she had to act.

She needed a high-tech ghoul to help.

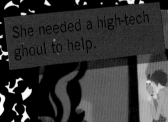

Ghoulia! I need your help.

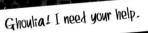

Ghoulia was so addicted to the game, she paid no attention!

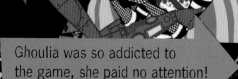

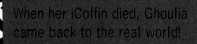

When her iCoffin died, Ghoulia came back to the real world!

So, Robecca shook Ghoulia hard and her iCoffin battery fell out.

Robecca explained that they needed to put a stop to the *Angry Ghouls* epidemic.

You're transmitting a virus to all other devices? Splendid!

Ghoulia's scheme worked. *Angry Ghouls* was wiped from every iCoffin.

Oh! Game over, I guess!

Until....

Yo! I got this rockin' new app. It's even better than Angry Ghouls!

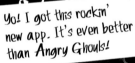

The student bodies came out of their gaming coma.

... with two obviously irritated exceptions.

Within seconds, every student body was staring at a screen again ...

Oh drear!

THE END

216

Inscare-itance

Grandmummy de Nile is keen to pass on her most valuable treasure to the granddaughter who proves her undying love. Will Cleo or Nefera triumph?

It was just another night in the crypt for the de Nile sisters.

You so owe me!

Consider it payback!

The dynastic duo were embroiled in their latest row ...

Riiing, Riiing

... when they were interrupted by a slave bringing the phone.

I got it!

No, it's for me!

As usual, they fought over who should answer it.

In fact, the call was for both ghouls.

Hello ghouls, it's your grandmummy.

Surely their grandmummy wouldn't be coming to visit?

Sadly she was, but she wasn't coming empty-handed.

I will give my most valuable treasure to the granddaughter who shows me she loves me the most.

Cleo immediately began her campaign to win the treasure ...

... by having an army of servants prepare a feast.

Nefera jealously watched Cleo's cooks parade a stream of delicious dishes. She'd only prepared one cupcake.

So she unleashed a plague of locusts ...

... which swiftly devoured Cleo's feast.

Undeterred, Cleo had the servants prepare a beautiful garden for Grandmummy.

Nefera had other plans.

In no time, Nefera's servants had dug a river through the middle of Cleo's garden.

The Pharaohs' curse upon you Nefera.

Next Cleo had her servant paint an enormous mural of Grandmummy.

She even signed it …

… just before Nefera defaced it with a moustache and beard.

Mwah, ha ha!

Poor Cleo had one last chance to prove herself worthy of Grandmummy's gift.

I know that Grandmummy collects these ancient jars.

You know what else she loves? Bowling!

I hereby give my most valuable treasure to Nefera!

Cleo was knocked flying and her jars smashed.

Just then, Grandmummy de Nile arrived by boat via Nefera's special river.

Yesss!

She immediately named her 'chosen one'.

Gloating Nefera threw open the treasure chest to find …

… the snarling, snapping Dog of the Dead!

Later that afternoon the perfect peace of the pyramid was only broken by …

… Nefera and her 'little treasure'.

THE END

CREATURE OF THE YEAR

There's an unexpected ogre-achiever at Monster High, but which faculty member will be chosen for Creature of the Year?

I've narrowed it down to two members of the Faculty.

Ladies, it's time for Monster High to pick its annual Creature of the Year!

Headmistress Bloodgood called the ghouls to her office.

The head asked the ghouls to help her choose the winner ...

... either Mr Hack ...

... or Mr Rotter.

There was a gasp of horror from the ghouls.

Lagoona was the first to speak.

Well it can't be Mr Hack — he's anti-phibean!

The bathing beauty showed the headmistress a memory.

They'd once been asked to nurture gargoyle eggs.

Maybe you should swap partners — everyone knows sea monsters are bad parents.

Mr Hack had insulted Lagoona.

219

Cleo agreed Mr Hack didn't deserve an award.

He takes royal delight in our misery.

She reminded them of the time he'd driven them ...

Your cabin is in a slightly different location.

... to Gloom Beach for fearleading trials.

He'd laughed himself half to death ...

It's, er, not that bad?

... at the fact they were staying in a dump.

All things considered ...

YOU FAILED!

YOU FAILED!

Bismuth | Molybdenum | Nitr

Mwah Hah Haaaa!

... everyone agreed that the mad science teacher ...

Off with their grades!

... was not quite the ticket!

That settles it, Mr Rotter it is!

The headmistress announced her decision.

Cleo was equally outraged at this suggestion.

Mr Rotter I did the work to perfection – why didn't I get an A?

I DON'T GIVE As!!

Frankie reminded everyone about Mr Rotter's other failings.

Remember when he gave us all detentions?